The MAILBOX® QUICK PLAY Language Arts

MW00651757

Group, Center, and Seatwork Activities

- Phonics and word recognition
- Literature
- Informational text

- Writing
- Conventions
- Vocabulary

30 key skills!

Managing Editor: Jennifer Bragg

Editorial Team: Becky S. Andrews, Diane Badden, Amy Butler Barsanti, Michelle Bayless, Stephanie Brachtenbach, Kimberley Bruck, Karen A. Brudnak, Amy Erickson Corkhill, Pam Crane, Chris Curry, David Drews, Barbara Duran, Kelli L. Gowdy, Tazmen Fisher Hansen, Marsha Heim, Lori Z. Henry, Laura Johnson, April LoTempio, Andrea O'Donnell, Beth Pallotta, Amy Payne, Mark Rainey, Greg D. Rieves, Kelly Robertson, Hope Rodgers-Medina, Rebecca Saunders, Hope Taylor Spencer, Donna K. Teal, Rachael Traylor, Sharon M. Tresino, Zane Williard, Virginia Zeletzki

www.themailbox.com

©2013 The Mailbox® Books
All rights reserved.
ISBN 978-1-61276-249-4

Printed in the United States
10 9 8 7 6 5 4 3 2 1   HPS246101

Table of Contents

COMMON CORE Aligned
www.themailbox.com/core

What's Inside

More than 150 activities on 30 key skills!

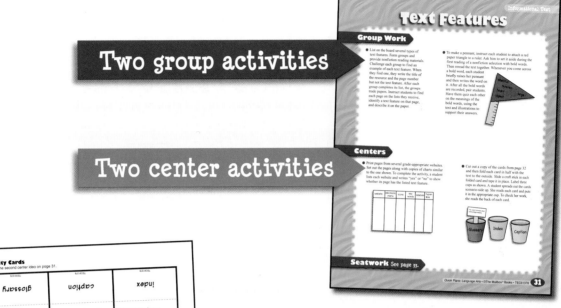

Two group activities

Two center activities

Patterns and more

One or more practice pages

Long and Short Vowels

Group Work

● Form two teams: one for long vowels and one for short vowels. Then give each team a sheet of chart paper titled with its assigned type of vowel and a few newspaper sports sections. The team members highlight in the newspapers words with their designated vowels and then list the words on their paper. When time is up, each team shares its list. The team with the longer list wins!

● Gather two blank cards per student and write a one-syllable long- or short-vowel word on each. Instruct each child to fold a sheet of paper in half lengthwise and then cut and label the top layer to make a flap for each vowel. Next, put two word cards on each student's desk. Then ask each child to walk from desk to desk with his paper. At each desk, he reads the word cards and writes the words under the corresponding flaps, distinguishing short and long vowels as shown.

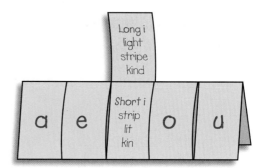

Centers

● Each student needs a copy of page 5. She reads each word and then underlines the short-vowel words with a red crayon and the long-vowel words with a blue crayon. She cuts out the cards and recording sheet. Then she glues each card in the correct column.

● *Partner Game:* Program blank cards with long- and short-vowel words, writing one word per card. For self-checking, write "L" or "S" on the back of each card. The players stack the cards faceup and draw a tic-tac-toe grid. In turn, each player takes the top card, reads its word, and then identifies it as a long- or a short-vowel word. He flips the card to check. If he is correct, he claims a tic-tac-toe space. If he is not correct, his turn is over. Play continues as in the traditional game.

Name **Teesha**   Recording sheet

Red for Short!

ă or ā	ĕ or ē	ĭ or ī	ŏ or ō	ŭ or ū
claim	bed	pinch	stone	scrub
tail	stem	pine	soap	cube
fan	steam	kin	toast	huge
clam	bead	kind	sop	just
faint	three	twin	toss	drum

soap

Seatwork See page 6.

claim	fan	bead	kin	soap
pinch	pine	drum	sop	kind
steam	bed	stone	faint	scrub
toast	tail	stem	three	clam
cube	toss	huge	twin	just

- -

Name _____ Recording sheet

Red for Short!

ă or ā	ĕ or ē	ĭ or ī	ŏ or ō	ŭ or ū

Meet Momma Martian!

Read each word.
Decide whether it is a short- or long-vowel word.
Color the letter in the matching column.

	short	long
1. toast	U	A
2. tot	S	R
3. glob	F	O
4. light	L	C
5. jump	V	N
6. lit	P	K
7. night	L	H
8. stem	B	T
9. smile	O	U
10. leaf	E	A
11. glass	R	E
12. block	Y	T

	short	long
13. teeth	S	F
14. claim	C	J
15. print	G	I
16. street	T	D
17. thick	O	E
18. tune	G	W
19. clam	U	E
20. wait	S	A
21. skip	D	I
22. globe	T	B
23. meet	P	M
24. bunch	R	O

What do you do when a baby alien cries?

To solve the riddle, write the letters that are *not* colored on the matching lines.

" __ __ __ __ - __ __ " __ __ __ __ __ __ __ __ __ __ __
  2   9 14   6 11 12   1   5 16 21   4   15   8   18 24 10 20

__ __ __ __ __ __ __ .
22   3   13   7 17 19 23

Bonus: How are the words *shade* and *wait* alike? How are they different? Write to describe the spelling patterns for the vowel sounds.

Quick Plans: Language Arts • ©The Mailbox® Books • TEC61378 • Key p. 94

Vowel Teams

Group Work

- Draw a large sports jersey on separate sheets of chart paper. Label each one with a different vowel team and a corresponding team name. Then display the posters. Students find words with the vowel teams in various reading materials and write them on the appropriate posters.

- Label the columns of a T chart with two vowel teams that have the same long-vowel sound. Program cards with corresponding words. Have students arrange their chairs in a circle and ask students to be seated. Next, display a card. Students read the word and identify its vowel team. Write the word on the chart and then direct each student to move one chair to the right if the word contains the first vowel team or two chairs to the left for the second vowel team. Continue with several words.

Centers

- **Partner Activity:** Use sticky dots to program each side of a die with a different vowel team. Provide a sand timer and reading materials. Partner 1 rolls the die, names the vowel team rolled, and then starts the sand timer. Each student looks for words with the vowel team and writes each one she finds. When time is up, the players compare their word lists. Then Partner 2 rolls the die to start a new round.

- **Partner Game:** A twosome cuts out a copy of the puzzle and word cards from page 8 and then puts the word cards in a bag. Next, the partners spread out the puzzle cards. A student draws a word card, finds the corresponding puzzle, and writes the word in the appropriate boxes. Whenever a child completes a puzzle by writing the last word, he takes the puzzle card. Partners alternate turns until all the puzzles are complete. The player with more puzzle cards wins.

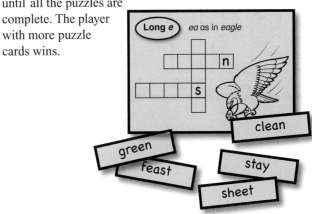

Seatwork See page 9.

Puzzle and Word Cards

Use with the second center activity on page 7.

Long e — ee as in *bee*

h   t

TEC61378

Long e — ea as in *eagle*

n

s

TEC61378

Long a — ai as in *paint*

h

s

TEC61378

Long a — ay as in *hay*

r

t

TEC61378

Long a — a_e as in *cake*

t

z

TEC61378

wheel	feast
raise	stay
jeans	sheet
spray	same
green	clean
maze	gray
snail	plane
chain	tape

   Quick Plans: Language Arts • ©The Mailbox® Books • TEC61378

Name _____

On the Loose

Write *ai*, *ay*, or *eigh* to complete each word.
Color a matching gumball for each answer.

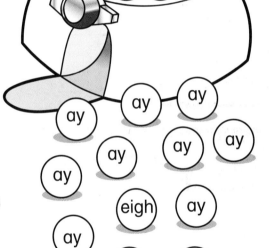

1. tod_____

2. cr_____on

3. sn_____l

4. spr_____n

5. _____teen

6. spr_____

7. cl_____

8. gr_____n

9. outw_____

10. r_____sin

11. h_____l

12. _____t

13. pl_____er

14. w_____st

15. d_____sy

16. _____ty

17. subw_____

18. tr_____l

19. del_____

20. _____th

21. m_____be

22. d_____light

23. n_____bor

24. w_____tless

Write the matching words from above.

1. ten more than 70 _____

2. stream of tiny drops _____

3. to make late _____

4. path _____

5. white and yellow flower _____

6. person who lives close by _____

Bonus: Write to sort the *ai*, *ay*, and *eigh* words above.

Multisyllable Words

Group Work

● Write 12 words with open and closed first syllables on separate blank cards. Cut between the syllables, scramble the cards, and display them facedown in a pocket chart. Have students play a Concentration game, matching cards by forming words and displaying the words they form. After all the words are formed, point out open and closed syllables and guide youngsters to draw conclusions about the corresponding vowel sounds.

● Draw a large soup can on each of three sheets of chart paper and number the cans from 1 to 3. Write one-, two-, and three-syllable food names on separate cards. Have youngsters read the words and attach the cards to the correct posters. Then invite each student to use the words shown and other food names to list ingredients for made-up soups.

Twelve-Syllable Stew

You need: carrots
cabbage
meatballs
potatoes
celery

Centers

● Program ice cream scoop cutouts with multisyllable words, writing each syllable on a different scoop. Also, set out ice cream dish cutouts. A student uses the scoops to form words on the dishes and then lists the words on a sheet of paper.

tor na do

● *Partner Game:* Set out a copy of the cards from page 11 (cut out) and a plastic disc with one side labeled "2" and one side labeled "3." Partners spread the cards out facedown. One player tosses the disc and then turns over the corresponding number of cards. If she can use two cards to form a compound word, she takes those cards and writes the word on a sheet of paper. Then if any card remains faceup, she flips it over. If she cannot form a compound word, her turn is over and she flips the cards back over. The partners take turns until no cards are left in play or no more words can be made. The player with more cards wins.

melon

paint

brush

3

Seatwork See page 12.

wash	play	side	light
TEC61378	TEC61378	TEC61378	TEC61378
house	mail	time	one
TEC61378	TEC61378	TEC61378	TEC61378
spring	paint	cloth	shell
TEC61378	TEC61378	TEC61378	TEC61378
ground	box	boat	drive
TEC61378	TEC61378	TEC61378	TEC61378
any	water	walk	melon
TEC61378	TEC61378	TEC61378	TEC61378
sail	egg	way	brush
TEC61378	TEC61378	TEC61378	TEC61378
yard	pole	back	flag
TEC61378	TEC61378	TEC61378	TEC61378

Brick by Brick

Cut apart the cards below.
Match each card with a closed first syllable to make a word.
Glue. Read.

1. num	2. ab	3. sum
4. pen	5. cab	6. sis
7. hap	8. in	9. fin
10. nap	11. con	12. bas

Write **true** or **false**.

_____ 1. Every syllable has at least one vowel.

_____ 2. A closed syllable ends with a consonant.

_____ 3. The vowel sound in most closed syllables is long.

_____ 4. When you finish saying a closed syllable, your mouth is open.

Bonus: Draw lines to divide each word into two syllables.

spinach   subtract   wagon   velvet   funny

mer	cil	ter	ket	sent	ber
py	sect	in	test	kin	ish

Irregularly Spelled Words

Group Work

● Display four irregularly spelled words and guide students to explain why the sound-spellings are not regular. Next, give each group of students a large sheet of paper. Have each group write a silly or realistic paragraph with the words and underline them. Then display the paragraphs. When it's time for a group to present its work, hand a group member a flashlight. Ask him to lead his group in reading the paragraph aloud and shine the light on the featured words when they come to them.

> Done has a silent *e*, but it does not have a long *o* sound.

● Write *me* and *go* near the top of a sheet of chart paper. Remind students that the words are open syllables, so the vowels are long. Then draw a large lasso and write the words *to* and *do* in it. Explain that these words are outlaw words since they don't fit the open-syllable pattern. Next, write familiar spelling patterns outside the lasso. As youngsters come across words that don't fit the patterns, invite them to "rope" the words in by writing them in the lasso.

Centers

● Set out copies of word searches that feature one irregularly spelled word each. Also set out a list of different irregular words and blank grid paper. A student uses a highlighter to complete a word search. Then she makes a word search with a listed word and leaves it for a different center visitor to complete.

other

o	b	k	r	e	s
t	g	t	e	i	n
h	o	t	h	e	r
e	t	u	t	r	e
r	h	h	o	c	h
a	e	a	s	o	t
n	r	e	h	t	o
o	t	h	e	r	m

● *Partner Game:* Set out student copies of page 14 and two different-colored pencils. To take a turn, a player connects two adjacent dots with a horizontal or vertical line and then reads the neighboring words. If he completes a box, he lightly colors it. The partners take turns until no more boxes can be made or time is up. Then they compare the number of boxes they each colored. The student with more colored boxes wins.

Names Diego Parker

Box Them Up!

said	they	what	were
could	water	many	done
both	move	warm	above
friend	pretty	doesn't	talk
would	their	again	give
once	been	people	does
enough	gone	most	know

Seatwork See page 15.

Names_____

Box Them Up!

●   ●   ●   ●   ●

said   they   what   were

●   ●   ●   ●   ●

could   water   many   done

●   ●   ●   ●   ●

both   move   warm   above

●   ●   ●   ●   ●

friend   pretty   doesn't   talk

●   ●   ●   ●   ●

would   their   again   give

●   ●   ●   ●   ●

once   been   people   does

●   ●   ●   ●   ●

enough   gone   most   know

●   ●   ●   ●   ●

Quick Plans: Language Arts • ©The Mailbox® Books • TEC61378

14   **Note to the teacher:** Use with the second center activity on page 13.

Name _____

Fresh at Flo's

Write the words to complete the story.
Use the word bank.

Word Bank

was	very	whole
pie	full	always
people	gone	love
berries	enough	only

Flo makes the _____ best pies. She puts so many fresh

_____ in them! Some _____ say that one

piece of pie isn't _____. They _____ Flo's

pies and _____ ask for more. Today, someone ordered

_____ one piece of berry _____. When that piece

was _____, she asked for another. She ended up eating the

_____ pie. In the end, she was _____ and the pie

plate _____ empty.

Circle the words *one* and *gone* above. Do they fit a spelling pattern you know? Why

or why not? _____

_____

_____

_____

Bonus: How are the words *piece* and *pie* alike? How are they different? Write to explain.

Prefixes and Suffixes

Group Work

● Label fish cutouts (patterns from page 17) each with a different prefix or suffix. Store the patterns in a bag or plastic fishbowl. Each day choose a student to "go fishing" by selecting a cutout from the container. Tape the fish to the board; write a word next to it that uses the prefix or suffix and then use the word in a sentence. Then challenge students to use context clues to determine the meaning of the affix and the whole word.

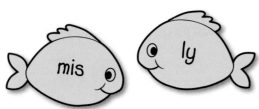

● Write a prefix or suffix on the board. Review its meaning and then have students name words that use the affix. Write the words on the board. Next, give each child five index cards. Direct the student to write on one card a title that uses the affix, such as *The* [-tion] *Book*. Then instruct the child to write a different word and its definition on each remaining card. Staple each student's cards together to make a booklet.

Centers

● Set out a dictionary and a list of words with prefixes or suffixes. A student selects a word from the list and writes it at the top of a sheet of paper. She then writes a definition of the word, writes a sentence using the word, and illustrates the sentence.

unload
unfold
unclip
uncooked
uneaten
unhurt
unhelpful
untrained

untrained
the opposite of trained
It was clear the dog was
untrained after it ate four
pairs of Mom's shoes.

● *Partner Game:* Draw a 16-box grid on a sheet of paper. Letter the horizontal axis and number the vertical axis. Program eight spaces with prefixes and eight with base words that, when combined with at least one prefix on the grid, make real words. Cover each space with a sticky note. In turn, students call out two grid locations. If a prefix and base word are read and they make a real word, the child keeps the sticky notes and takes another turn. If not, his turn is over. Play continues until all the spaces are uncovered or all possible words have been made.

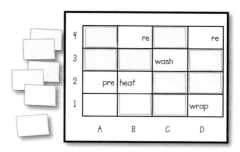

Seatwork See page 18.

Buzzing About a Birthday

Match each pair of symbols. Write each word.

● re-	⊙ matched	◐ _____
◐ pre-	◐ heat	⊖ _____
◑ like	◒ -ly	⊙ _____
◗ dis-	◐ -ness	◑ _____
⊙ mis-	☺ -est	◒ _____
⊖ help	● start	◐ _____
⊜ quick	⊖ -ful	◒ _____
◒ pain	⊗ afraid	● _____
☺ sweet	◐ neat	☺ _____
⊗ un-	◒ -less	⊗ _____

Use the words from above to complete the story.

It was two hours before the party when the power went out! My sister was scared

but I was _____. I had been in plenty of storms before, so I knew all
                          1

we could do was wait. When the power finally came back on, we _____
                                                                                    2

got to work in the kitchen. First, we had to _____ the computer to
                                                          3

pull up the cake recipe. Then we had to _____ the oven. My
                                                       4

_____ sister mixed the batter while I made the punch. After the
        5

cake came out of the oven, we both coated it with the

_____ icing on the planet. "There's no
        6

way Mom will _____ this cake!" my
                          7

sister exclaimed. We put out _____
                                          8

plates and forks just in time to yell "Surprise" as Mom

walked in the door. It was a "bee-utiful" birthday for her!

Bonus: Find the two words on the list that were not used in the story. Write a sentence with each word.

Latin Suffixes

Group Work

● Write words that use Latin suffixes on paper strips. Also list the words on the board. Direct students to read the word list and identify the suffix in each word. Underline each suffix and discuss how it changes the meaning of the whole word. Next, invite a child to select a card and draw on the board a picture that depicts its meaning. Have the student call on classmates to identify the word. Choose a different youngster to select another card and continue.

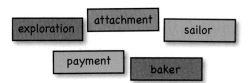

● Write four different suffixes on separate cards and post each card on a different wall. Next, write a base word on the board. At your signal, have students decide which suffix makes a real word when added to the base word and then move to that wall. When all students are settled, have each group say the resulting word. If the group's word is a real word, the students continue to the next round. If not, they sit down. Repeat with a new base word until one student is left standing or time is up.

Centers

● Program copies of the tree pattern on page 20 with different suffixes. Provide a class supply of blank leaves (patterns on page 20), a dictionary, and tape. A child chooses a tree and writes on a leaf a word that uses the corresponding suffix. She writes the word's meaning on the leaf and then confirms her work with the dictionary before taping the leaf to the tree.

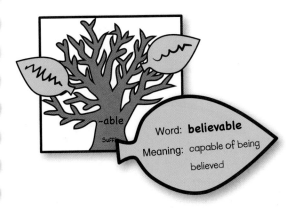

● Label cubes with base words and suffixes. If desired, write the meaning of each suffix on the opposite face of the block. A child chooses a base word and places next to it each suffix block that, when added to the base word, makes a real word. He writes each word and its meaning on a sheet of paper; then he continues with the other base words.

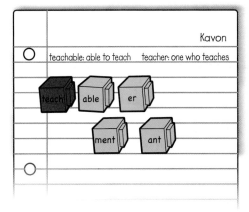

Seatwork See page 21.

Tree and Leaf Patterns

Use with the first center activity on page 19.

Suffix

TEC61378

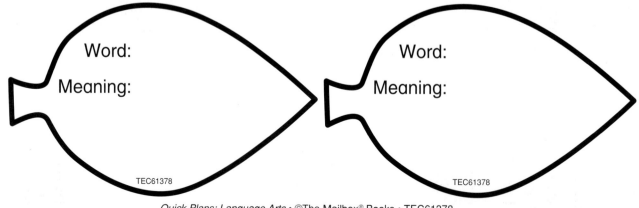

Word:

Meaning:

Word:

Meaning:

TEC61378

TEC61378

Name _____

That's One Fast Fox!

For each base word, add a suffix to make a real word.
Write the word under the matching heading.
Then write the meaning of each word.
Hint: Do not change the spelling of any base words.

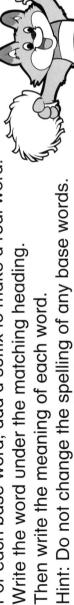

-able (capable of)

-er (one who or that)

-ment (an act of)

Base Words

cheerlead

govern

break

improve

measure

work

move

play

sprint

travel

manage

print

Bonus: Write and define one more word for each suffix.

Story Elements

Group Work

● After a small group reads a story, set out a copy of page 23. Have each student, in turn, use a paper clip and a pencil to spin the spinner. Ask him to read the question on which the spinner lands, answer it, and tell whether his answer is based on information from the illustrations, the text, or both.

● Program sentence strips with story-element questions that compare two stories. Then post the questions around the room. After students read two versions of a story, form as many groups as there are questions. Then instruct each group to go to a different question. Have the students in each group read their question and discuss it among themselves for two minutes. Then signal each group to move to the next question. Once each group discusses all the questions, gather students and invite them to share the main points of their discussions.

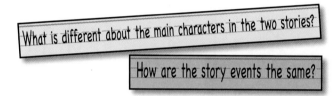

What is different about the main characters in the two stories?

How are the story events the same?

Centers

● *Partner Activity:* Draw a grid with three-inch squares and write a different plot-related question on each square. Then secure the paper to the bottom of a shallow box. Cover each question with a three-inch square sticky note and set out a plastic disc. Partner 1 tosses the disc onto the grid. He lifts the sticky note on which the disc lands and reads aloud the question. Partner 2 answers it. Then they trade roles.

● To follow up a familiar story, label a top hat cutout and attach it to a paper lunch bag as shown. Then open and stand the bag. Write on each of several blank cards an alternate setting, character detail, or plot detail. Then put the cards in the bag. A student takes a card and writes how the story would change if that detail were part of it.

What is the most important story event? Why?

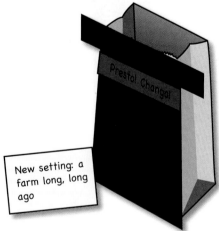

Presto! Change!

New setting: a farm long, long ago

Seatwork See page 24.

Spin and Tell!

Story elements

What is one interesting detail about the setting?

Which character do you like the most? Why?

Did the story end as you expected? Explain.

If you could ask the author a question about the story events, what would it be? Why?

Quick Plans: Language Arts • ©The Mailbox® Books • TEC61378

Note to the teacher: Use with the first group activity on page 22.

23

Name _____

24

Story in Full Bloom

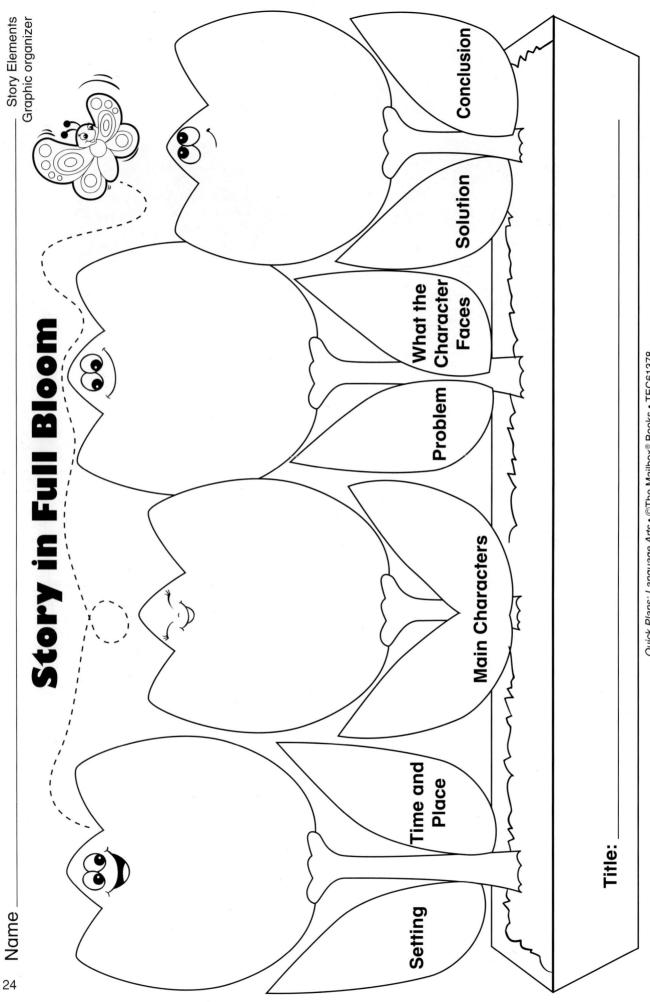

Setting

Time and Place

Main Characters

Problem

What the Character Faces

Solution

Conclusion

Title: _____

Quick Plans: Language Arts • ©The Mailbox® Books • TEC61378

Note to the teacher: After a child reads a story, have her complete a copy of this page by writing the story elements on the blossoms.

Story Structure

Group Work

● Make a poster for each part of a story (beginning, middle, and end) with a title and the corresponding questions shown. Display the posters in your reading area. They're a great reference when students recap stories!

Beginning
 Who are the main characters?
 Where and when does the story take place?

Middle
 What is the problem?
 How do the characters try to solve it?

End
 How is the problem solved?
 Do any characters change? If so, how?

● Have each student jot story events as you read a story aloud. After you finish reading, instruct each youngster to write one event on a sticky note and then attach it to a class poster with three labeled columns ("Beginning," "Middle," and "End"). Cut apart the columns. Then form three groups and give each group a column. Each group arranges its sticky notes in chronological order, stacking any duplicates and adding any significant events that are missing. Then they refer to the notes as they write a summary.

Centers

● A student writes his name and the title of a familiar book where indicated on a copy of page 26. He recaps the beginning, middle, and end of the story. Then he cuts out the patterns and cuts two slits in the top of the paper strip where indicated. Next, he folds the paper strip on the thin lines and glues the ends together. Finally, he illustrates the back of the title card and slides it into the slits.

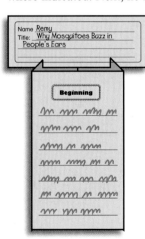

● *Partner Activity:* To review the parts of a story, write story events on blank cards. Also write "B," "M," or "E" to indicate the beginning, middle, or end of the story. Set out the cards and book. The partners stack the cards facedown. They take turns reading the cards aloud and having one another identify the corresponding part of the story, referring to the book as needed.

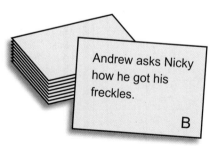

Andrew asks Nicky how he got his freckles.

B

Seatwork See page 27.

3-D Graphic Organizer Patterns

Use with the first center idea on page 25.

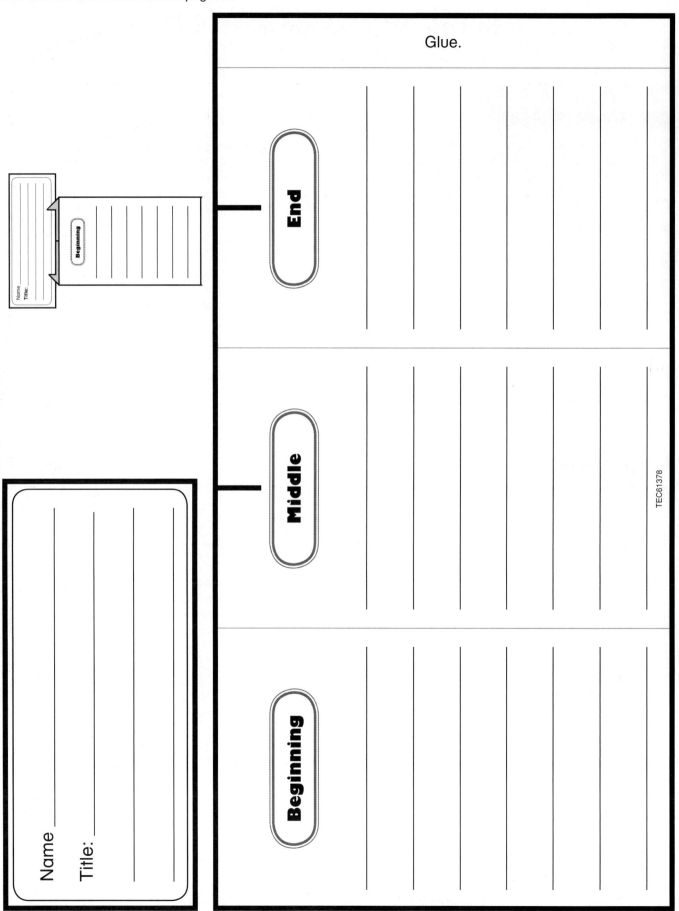

Quick Plans: Language Arts • ©The Mailbox® Books • TEC61378

Name _____

A Story to Ponder

Title: _____

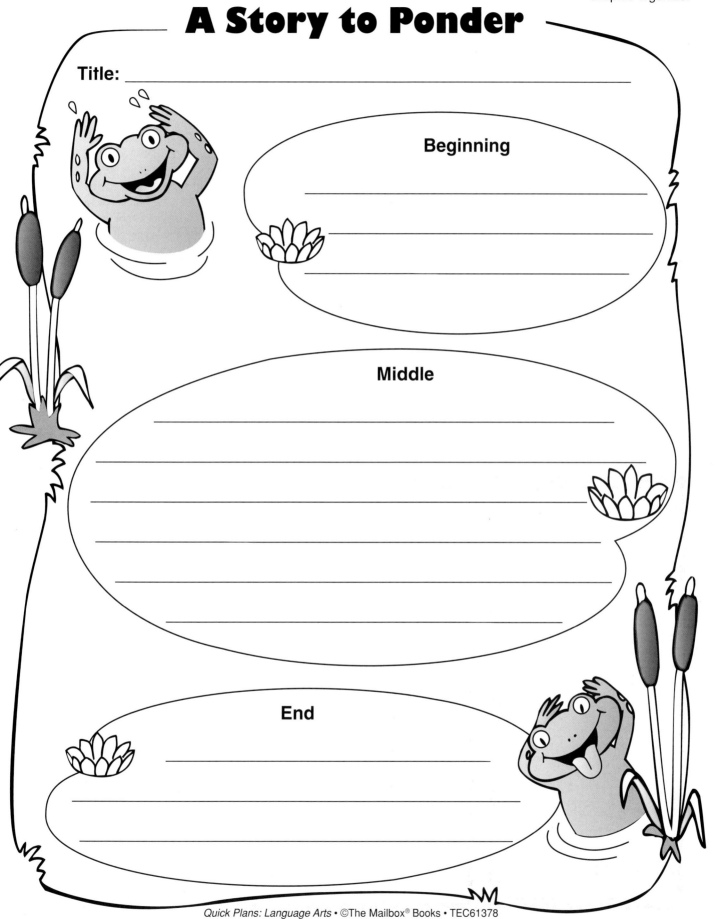

Beginning

_____

_____

_____

Middle

_____

_____

_____

_____

_____

End

_____

_____

_____

Quick Plans: Language Arts • ©The Mailbox® Books • TEC61378

Note to the teacher: After a student reads a story or listens to one, have him recap it on a copy of this page.

Character Analysis

Group Work

● After students read a book with well-developed characters, write the main character's name on the board. Have students brainstorm adjectives that describe the character, verbs that tell what the character does, and nouns that are synonyms for the character. Then guide each student to use the format shown to write a poem about the character.

Line 1: Character's name
Line 2: Adjective, adjective
Line 3: Verb, verb, verb
Line 4: Four-word phrase that tells about the character
Line 5: Noun (another word for the character)

● For this reading group idea, cut several speech bubbles from sticky notes, keeping some adhesive at the top. Have each student infer what an assigned character thinks or feels during a certain story event, write the information on a speech bubble cutout, and then attach the cutout to the corresponding page in the book. Invite each youngster to tell the group what she wrote and why.

Centers

● To follow up a story, write significant story events on separate blank cards and the name of a relevant character on each one. Set out the cards, the book, and student copies of page 29. A student takes a card at random. He writes the character's name and the event on his paper. Then he completes the paper, referring to the book as needed.

● *Partner Activity:* Make a word search with words that describe traits and feelings of two or more characters. Set out copies of the word search, a list of the characters, two highlighters, and paper. Each partner lists the character names on her paper. To take a turn, a partner highlights a word in the puzzle. She names a character that demonstrates that trait or feeling, identifies supporting story details, and writes the word with the character's name on her paper. After the partners complete the puzzle, they compare their lists.

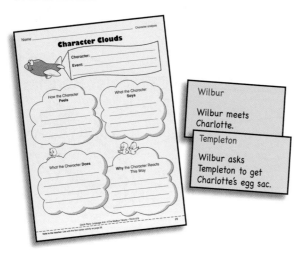

Seatwork See page 30.

Character Clouds

Character: _____

Event: _____

_____

How the Character **Feels**

_____

_____

_____

What the Character **Says**

_____

_____

_____

What the Character **Does**

_____

_____

_____

Why the Character Reacts This Way

_____

_____

_____

Quick Plans: Language Arts • ©The Mailbox® Books • TEC61378

"Whoooo" Stars in the Story?

Title: _____

Main character: _____

Words That Describe the Character
at the **Beginning**

Words That Describe the Character
at the **End**

Evidence From the Story

Evidence From the Story

Note to the teacher: After a student reads a story, give her a copy of this page to complete. Instruct her to write words that describe a main character at the beginning and end of the story and then write details from the text and illustrations that support her word choices.

Text Features

Group Work

- List on the board several types of text features. Form groups and provide nonfiction reading materials. Challenge each group to find an example of each text feature. When they find one, they write the title of the resource and the page number but not the text feature. After each group completes its list, the groups trade papers. Instruct students to find each page on the lists they receive, identify a text feature on that page, and describe it on the paper.

- To make a pennant, instruct each student to attach a red paper triangle to a ruler. Ask him to set it aside during the first reading of a nonfiction selection with bold words. Then reread the text together. Whenever you come across a bold word, each student briefly raises her pennant and then writes the word on it. After all the bold words are recorded, pair students. Have them quiz each other on the meanings of the bold words, using the text and illustrations to support their answers.

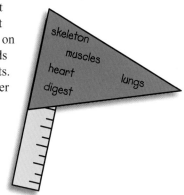

Centers

- Print pages from several grade-appropriate websites. Set out the pages along with copies of charts similar to the one shown. To complete the activity, a student lists each website and writes "yes" or "no" to show whether its page has the listed text feature.

website	electronic menu	icons	key words	sidebars	hyper-links

- Cut out a copy of the cards from page 32 and then fold each card in half with the text to the outside. Slide a craft stick in each folded card and tape it in place. Label three cups as shown. A student spreads out the cards scenario-side up. She reads each card and puts it in the appropriate cup. To check her work, she reads the back of each card.

Seatwork See page 33.

Activity Cards

Use with the second center idea on page 31.

glossary	caption	index
TEC61378	*TEC61378*	*TEC61378*
You want to know what *camouflage* means.	You want to know the name of the animal shown in a picture.	You want to know where in a book it tells what tree frogs eat.

index	glossary	caption
TEC61378	*TEC61378*	*TEC61378*
You have a turtle book and only want to read the part about sea turtles.	You need the definition of *habitat*.	You want to know more about a photograph that shows lions.

caption	caption	glossary
TEC61378	*TEC61378*	*TEC61378*
Your teacher asks what is happening in a picture. You aren't sure.	A friend asks what kind of plant is shown in a picture.	You want to define the word *predator*.

index	index	glossary
TEC61378	*TEC61378*	*TEC61378*
You wonder whether a book about dogs explains how to train them.	You want to find out whether a book about the rain forest tells about sloths.	You're reading a book about dinosaurs and forget what *herbivore* means.

Quick Plans: Language Arts • ©The Mailbox® Books • TEC61378

Name _____

It's for the Birds!

Use the index of Kit's bird-watching book to answer the questions.

Index
beaks, 6, 10, 33
blue jays, 34
ducks, 36
eggs
    colors, 6, 7
    hatching, 5, 6
    laying, 4
    size, 7, 37
finches, 35
flightless birds, 9, 50
migration, 36, 42

nests
    common, 25, 26
    making, 24
    uncommon, 27, 55
penguins, 50
robins, 34
seagulls, 38
storks, 40
swans, 59
wings
    feathers, 12
    flying, 16, 18, 22
    speed, 13

1. On what page can Kit read about robins? _____

2. Kit wants to find out about birds that can't fly. What are the best pages for her to check?

_____ and _____

3. Kit wonders whether bird beaks are sharp. What pages should she check?

_____, _____, and _____

4. What are the names of two kinds of birds Kit can read about?

_____ on page _____
_____ on page _____

5. On what pages might Kit find out what *migration* means?

_____ and _____

6. Kit wants to find out what kind of nest she saw yesterday. What pages should she check?

_____, _____, _____, and _____

7. Kit needs to write a report about how wings help birds fly. What pages should she check?

_____, _____, and _____

8. Kit wants to know how long it takes eggs to hatch. What pages should she check?

_____ and _____

Bonus: Write two ways an index can be helpful.

Main Idea and Details

Group Work

● Laminate a paper road and a blank road sign and display them with the title shown. After students read a nonfiction selection, have them identify the main idea. Then use a wipe-off marker to write it on the street sign. Instruct youngsters to name details in the text that support the main idea; then write them on the road.

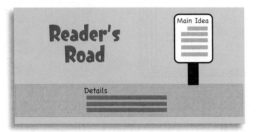

● Give each student a multiparagraph nonfiction reading selection and then read it together. Next, form groups and give each group a sheet of chart paper. Reread the selection with students one paragraph at a time. After each paragraph, instruct each group to write the main idea in their own words. Then invite the groups to share their topic sentences and name supporting details.

Centers

● Set out a brief nonfiction selection along with student copies of page 35, large sheets of construction paper, and blank cards. A student reads the selection. Then she writes the main idea on a card and a supporting detail on each arrow. After she cuts out the arrows, she glues the card and arrows to a sheet of paper as shown.

● *Partner Activity:* Each partner chooses a different paragraph from a nonfiction selection. He writes each sentence from the paragraph and an irrelevant sentence on separate blank cards and then shuffles them. Next, the partners trade cards. Each partner reads the sentences he receives, determines which sentence is irrelevant, and then sets it aside. He identifies the main idea of the remaining sentences and explains why the sentence he put aside is irrelevant. Then the partners put each group of cards in a separate plastic bag for future center visitors.

Seatwork See page 36.

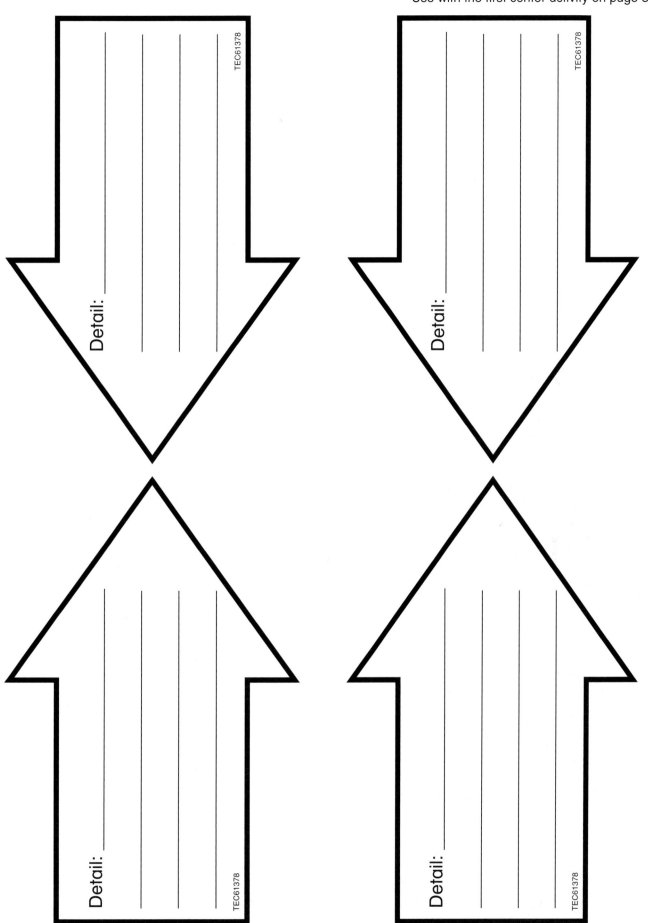

Detail: _____

Detail: _____

Detail: _____

Detail: _____

TEC61378

TEC61378

TEC61378

TEC61378

Name _____

Whale Wonders

Cut apart the cards. Sort the sentences by topic.
Write the main idea for each group.
Glue each sentence below the matching main idea.

Main idea: _____	Main idea: _____
_____	_____
_____	_____

Bonus: How do the sentences in the first group relate to the main idea?

Quick Plans: Language Arts • ©The Mailbox® Books • TEC61378 • Key p. 94

Whales have smooth skin that slides through water.	Whales can hear high and low sounds.
Some whales use sounds to find objects underwater.	Many whales can swim very fast.
People cannot hear some sounds that whales can hear.	Whales can hold their breath underwater for a long time.
Strong muscles in a whale's tail help it swim quickly.	Some whales attract other whales by making sounds.

Opinion Writing

Group Work

● Display opinions in different classroom areas, each with a chart like the one shown. Assign students to each display. Ask each group member to write his name below "Yes" or "No," and encourage students to list different reasons for their opinions. Have each group rotate to each chart. To follow up, use the charts to jump-start individual writing practice.

Students should have homework every night.

Do you agree?	Reasons
Yes	1. 2. 3. 4. 5.
No	1. 2. 3. 4. 5.

● Write topics on separate blank cards and put them in a container. List on the board linking words for connecting opinions and reasons, such as *because* and *since*. Have a student take a card, read the topic, and state an opinion about it. Next, invite a volunteer to use a linking word as she supports the opinion and links arms with the student. After her classmates identify the linking word, continue with different students and topics.

Centers

● To make a spinner, divide a circle cutout into quarters and write a different topic in each quarter. Set out the spinner, a paper clip, a pencil, a list of linking words, colored pencils, and writing paper. A student uses the paper clip and pencil to spin the spinner. Next, she writes the topic she spins. She writes a relevant opinion and uses linking words as she writes three or more sentences that support her opinion. Then she uses colored pencils to underline the linking words she used.

Linking Words

also	however
because	in order to
due to	since
for example	so that
for instance	therefore

● Set out a list of topics, colorful copies of page 38, black paper, scissors, and glue. A student writes a topic on a copy of page 38. He writes a relevant opinion, three supporting statements, and a conclusion. Then he cuts the puzzle pieces apart, and glues the pieces in place on a sheet of paper, allowing the paper to show between the pieces.

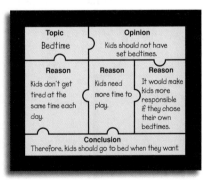

Seatwork See page 39.

Puzzle Pattern

Use with the second center idea on page 37.

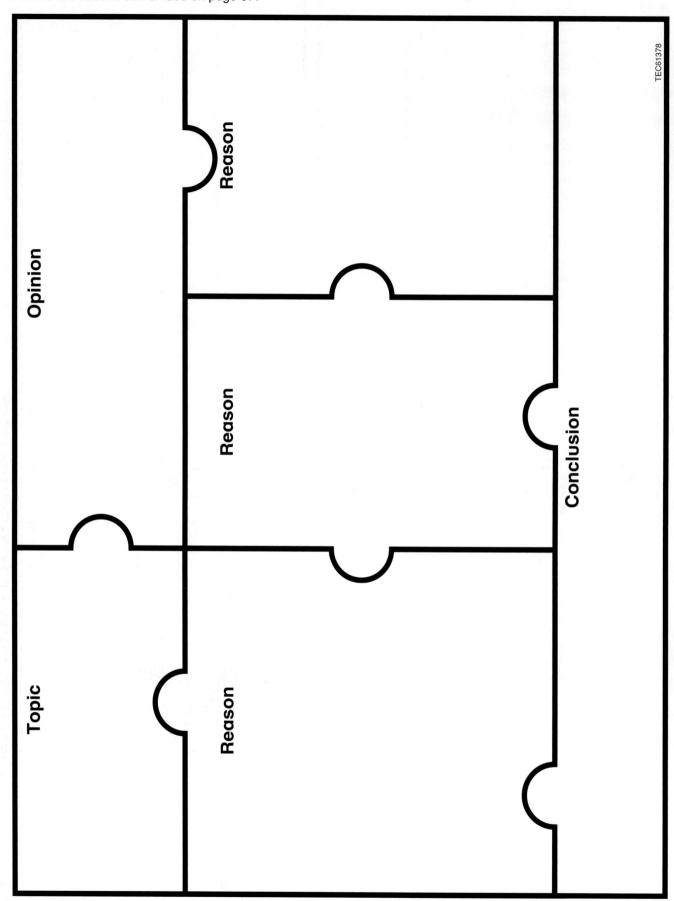

TEC61378

Quick Plans: Language Arts • ©The Mailbox® Books • TEC61378

Writing Aweigh!

Topic

Opinion

Reason

Reason

Reason

Conclusion

Quick Plans: Language Arts • ©The Mailbox® Books • TEC61378

Note to the teacher: Before a student writes an opinion piece, have him plan his writing on a copy of this page.

Informative and Explanatory Writing

Group Work

● Form small groups and give each group a math problem. Have the students write and illustrate a paragraph that explains how to solve the problem. Then invite a student from each group to present her group's work to the class. As she reads the paragraph, ask her classmates to follow the instructions exactly. Follow up with a discussion of any confusions or inaccuracies.

● Give each youngster two index cards. Instruct her to write on each card a different school-related fact that would be helpful to a transfer student. Then ask students to read their facts aloud and display them in a pocket chart, grouping like topics. Next, form small groups, give each group one or more sets of cards, and have students write paragraphs with the corresponding information. Then compile students' work into a class guide.

> Lunch is at 11:35.
>
> If you want a hot lunch, you need to buy a ticket.

Centers

● Set out an assortment of informative texts and a small paper bag. Display a list of two or three features of good informative writing. A child uses sticky notes to flag features he finds in the selections. He writes on separate index cards why he thinks the flagged items are good examples. Then he puts the cards in the bag. After all the students visit the center, review their examples and comments and make a class list of things good nonfiction writers do.

● Provide nonfiction books about animals. A student uses sticky notes to flag in one or more books four interesting facts about a chosen animal. Next, she folds the sides of a sheet of construction paper to the center and cuts four flaps as shown. She writes on each flap a fact about the animal without naming the animal. Then she unfolds the paper, writes the animal's name, and illustrates it. Finally, she adds her work to a display titled "What Could It Be?"

> **Things to Look For**
> Great titles
> Interesting introductions
> Clear organization

Sha[rk]

It lives in the ocean.

It is a meat-eater.

It has a boneless skeleton.

Seatwork See pages 41 and 42.

Give It a Whirl!

How to
_____
_____

Note to the teacher: Use this page when students write step-by-step instructions. A student completes the heading on a copy of this page. Then she writes numbered steps in separate sections of the ball.

Name _____

Writing
Informative/explanatory

Take Note!

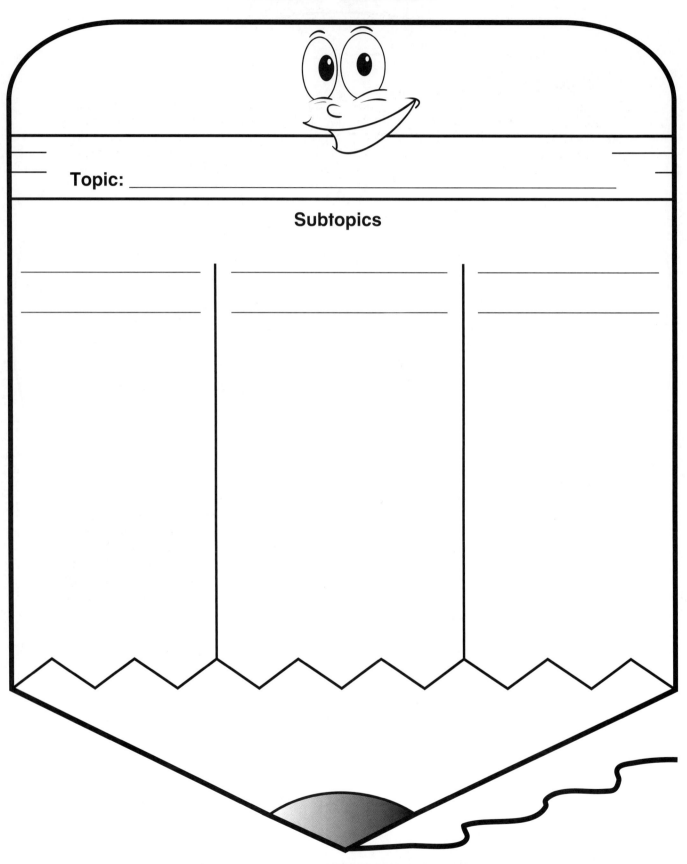

Topic: _____

Subtopics

Quick Plans: Language Arts • ©The Mailbox® Books • TEC61378

Note to the teacher: Use this page when students need to take notes on a topic before writing about it. A child writes the topic and three
42 subtopics where indicated. Then he jots notes about the subtopics in the appropriate columns.

Personal Narrative

Group Work

- Lead students in discussing what makes a memory special. Then invite volunteers to each share a favorite memory. Direct each student to decorate the child outline on a copy of page 44 so that it looks like herself. When she is satisfied with her illustration, she writes in the thought bubble about her favorite memory, including details that describe her thoughts, feelings, and actions.

- Direct each child to divide and label a sheet of construction paper (gift) as shown. Also have each student cut out and glue a construction paper bow to the top of his resulting graphic organizer. Next, instruct each child to think of a time he gave a special gift. Then have him complete his graphic organizer. Finally, lead each student to refer to his organizer as he writes a personal narrative on a separate sheet of paper.

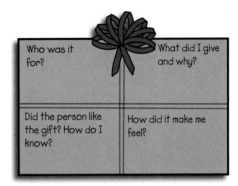

Centers

- Write identifying labels on the backs of photos of your class participating in school activities. A child chooses a photo and recalls the sequence of events that occurred when the photo was taken. Then she writes a personal narrative to tell about the details of the activity.

- *Partner Activity:* Gather a supply of mementos that might evoke personal memories in children. A twosome chooses one item that makes both students recall a special time. Then each student writes a personal story based on the item. The pair binds the stories between construction paper covers, adds a title like the one shown, and draws an illustration of the item.

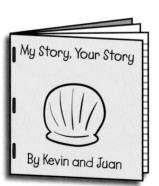

Seatwork See page 45.

Name _____

A Memorable Moment

Quick Plans: Language Arts • ©The Mailbox® Books • TEC61378

44   **Note to the teacher:** Use with the first group activity on page 43.

Name _____

Up, Up, and Away!

Think about a time you were excited.

When was it?

Where were you?

Who was with you?

What were you doing?

Why were you excited?

Bonus: Write a personal narrative using the ideas from your organizer.

Quick Plans: Language Arts • ©The Mailbox® Books • TEC61378

45

Imaginative Narrative

Group Work

- To prepare, cover a classroom door with bulletin board paper and write a prompt, like the one shown, across the top. Have students complete the sentence as you write their ideas on the paper. Then direct each child to use the ideas on the door to write his own imaginative narrative response to the prompt.

I found a secret door in my grandmother's attic. When I pushed it open...

...I saw a tunnel!

...a mouse jumped out!

...there was a magic garden.

- Direct students to sit in six small groups with their writing journals. Cut apart a copy of page 47 and give a card to one student in each group. Have her read the card's number and prompt. Then direct each group member to write in her journal the prompt's number and notes and ideas the prompt inspires. After a couple minutes, give a signal and have each group pass its card to the group on the left and repeat the activity. Continue until each group has read and responded to each prompt. At a later date, guide each child to choose one idea from her notes and write an imaginative story about it.

Centers

- Post an imaginative prompt. A child folds a sheet of paper in half, cuts three slits through one layer as shown, and labels each flap with a story element. He opens each flap and sketches corresponding images. Then he uses his sketches to write an imaginative narrative response to the prompt on a separate sheet of paper.

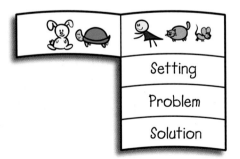

Setting

Problem

Solution

- Divide three paper plates (spinners) each into six sections. In each section of one spinner, write different ways a story might begin. In each section of another spinner, write different problems that might happen in the middle of a story. In each section of the third spinner, write ways a story might end. A child uses a paper clip and a pencil to spin each spinner. Then she uses the ideas spun to write a story.

Seatwork See page 48.

① 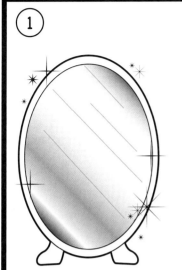 You find a magic mirror that will allow anyone in the world to appear before you. Tell about who you would choose to appear and what you would do or say.

TEC61378

② One of your toys comes to life! Write about how you and the toy would spend the day.

TEC61378

③ 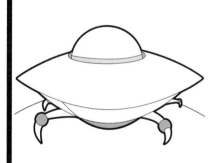 A UFO lands in your yard! Write to tell who or what is inside and what happens when they get out!

TEC61378

④ You find a magic scooter that will take you anywhere you want to go. Write about where you go and what happens when you get there.

TEC61378

⑤  You find a giant egg! Write to tell what happens when it hatches.

TEC61378

⑥ You are surprised to get a package in the mail. What happens when you open the box?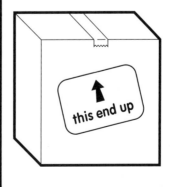

this end up

TEC61378

Spare Change

Choose a prompt.
Complete the graphic organizer.

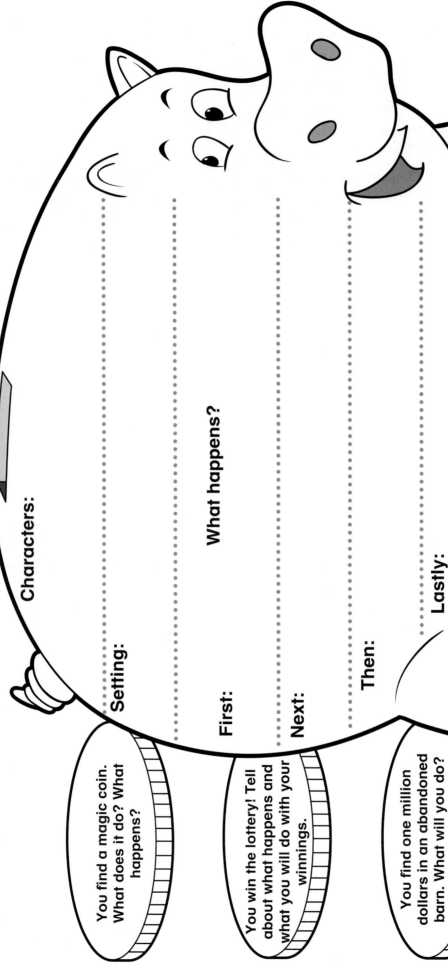

Characters:

Setting:

What happens?

First:

Next:

Then:

Lastly:

You find a magic coin. What does it do? What happens?

You win the lottery! Tell about what happens and what you will do with your winnings.

You find one million dollars in an abandoned barn. What will you do? Explain.

Bonus: Write a story using the ideas from your organizer.

Quick Plans: Language Arts • ©The Mailbox® Books • TEC61378

Nouns

Group Work

● Write a collective or abstract noun on each of 12 blank cards. Then form 12 groups. In turn, have each group take a card and act out the noun. After a classmate correctly guesses the noun, tape the card onto a labeled sheet of chart paper and keep the resulting word list posted as a reference.

● Gather one blank card for every two students and write a different abstract noun pair from the list shown on each one. Cut the cards to separate the pairs. Give each student a card and a sheet of paper. Then ask students to walk around the room and find the classmate whose card has a noun that is the opposite of his noun. When he finds her, they write a sentence with each noun. Repeat the activity until each student writes several sentences.

Abstract Nouns

beauty, ugliness	love, hatred
bravery, cowardliness	pride, embarrassment
childhood, adulthood	strength, weakness
fact, fiction	success, failure
happiness, sadness	trust, distrust
honesty, dishonesty	truth, lie
knowledge, ignorance	work, play

Centers

● Provide old magazines and newspapers and a list of collective nouns for student examples. A student either illustrates a collective noun or cuts out a picture that represents a collective noun and then glues it to a sheet of paper. She writes a caption that includes the noun and the appropriate verb form. Then she circles the collective noun.

● Set out a copy of the spinner from page 50 and a highlighter. A student uses a paper clip and pencil to spin the spinner. After he reads the nouns he spins, he writes a sentence with one of them. Then he highlights the noun and the corresponding verb. He continues until he writes several sentences with different nouns.

Collective Nouns

band of musicians	gaggle of geese
cast of characters	herd of horses
class of students	pride of lions
cluster of grapes	set of tools
deck of cards	swarm of bees

Seatwork See page 51.

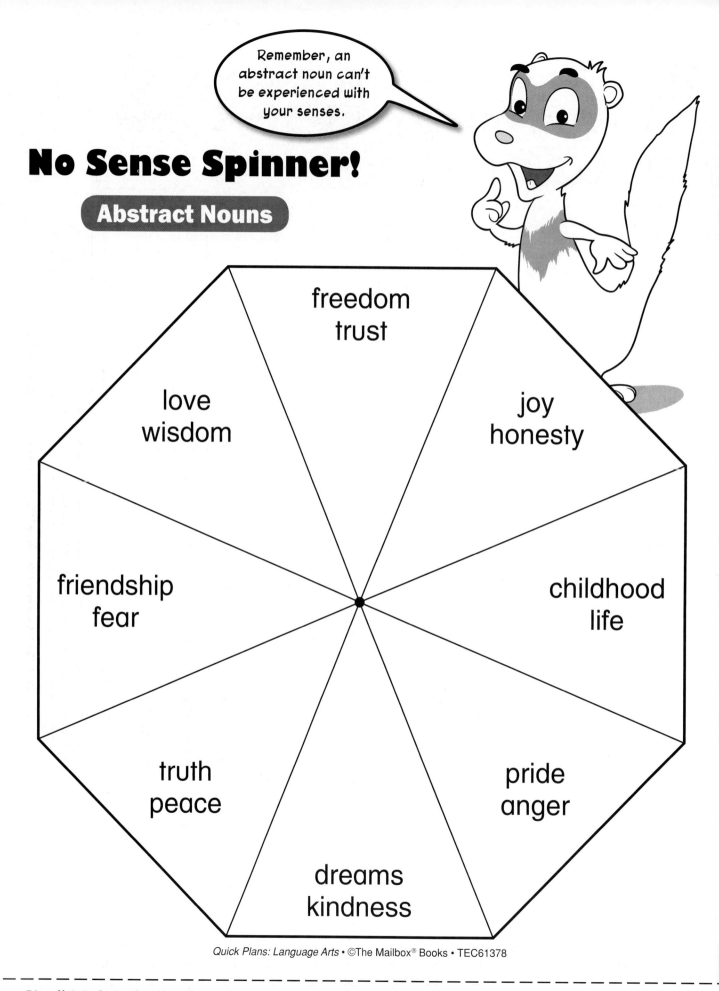

No Sense Spinner!

Abstract Nouns

Remember, an abstract noun can't be experienced with your senses.

freedom
trust

love
wisdom

joy
honesty

friendship
fear

childhood
life

truth
peace

pride
anger

dreams
kindness

Quick Plans: Language Arts • ©The Mailbox® Books • TEC61378

Note to the teacher: Use with the second center idea on page 49.

Name _____

Nouns
Collective nouns

Moving Day

People		

Things		

Circle each collective noun.
Write it in the matching box.

1. Tanner and his family are moving.

2. Tanner's father got a job with a new company.

3. There is a grove of trees in front of their new home.

4. Tanner's mother packed a set of china and a bunch of pans.

5. Mr. Brown will be on a building committee.

6. Tanner wants to pack his best deck of cards.

7. Tanner needs a box for his fleet of toy ships.

8. He packs his coin collection last.

9. Tanner helped his father pack a bundle of wood.

10. Tanner's mother thinks the staff at the new school is friendly.

11. Tanner's new class and chess club are nice too.

12. He can't wait to join the soccer team!

Bonus: Write three sentences with collective nouns for animals, such as a *herd of horses*.

Quick Plans: Language Arts • ©The Mailbox® Books • TEC61378 • Key p. 95

51

Plural Nouns

Group Work

● Pair students and have each twosome quickly list singular nouns and their plural forms. When time is up, each pair, in turn, reads its list aloud. If any other students listed the word pair, each twosome crosses it out. After youngsters compare how many of their word pairs are not crossed out, guide them to name the plural rules for those words.

● Write on sticky notes eight singular words for each of the following categories: add *s*, add *es*, change *y* to *i* and add *es*, and irregular. Form four teams, one for each category. Label four corresponding columns on the board. Then give each student a programmed sticky note. The teams take turns reading a word, identifying its plural form, and attaching it to the matching column. The first team to get eight words in its column wins.

Centers

● *Partner Game:* Program a copy of page 53 with the plural forms to make an answer key. Cut out the cards on a second copy. One student deals the cards evenly, and then each child stacks his cards facedown. To take a turn, a player turns over his top card, reads the noun, and spells its plural form. His partner checks the answer key. If the plural is misspelled, the player puts the card in the kitty. If it is spelled correctly, he keeps the card and takes any cards in the kitty. If he turns over a direction card, he puts that card and two others he has kept in the kitty. Players take turns until no cards are left in play. The player with more cards wins.

● Display a color code like the one shown. Write singular nouns on separate blank cards. A student takes a designated number of cards and lists the plural form of each word. Then she draws a star, check mark, or smiley face beside each word according to the code.

Color Code
Add *s*. = red
Add *es*. = blue
Change *y* to *i* and add *es*. = green
Other = orange

Seatwork See page 54.

candy TEC61378	tray TEC61378	monkey TEC61378	toolbox TEC61378
mess TEC61378	hobby TEC61378	radish TEC61378	company TEC61378
factory TEC61378	jelly TEC61378	toy TEC61378	key TEC61378
birthday TEC61378	story TEC61378	valley TEC61378	glass TEC61378
wrench TEC61378	brush TEC61378	penny TEC61378	memory TEC61378
donkey TEC61378	dress TEC61378	fairy TEC61378	walrus TEC61378
day TEC61378	butterfly TEC61378	spray TEC61378	pony TEC61378
compass TEC61378	**Phooey!** Give up three. TEC61378	**Zap!** Put three in. TEC61378	**Uh-oh!** Three have to go. TEC61378

Name _____

Roped In!

Write the plural form of each word to complete the sentences.
You will not use two words.

Word Bank

horse	bench
child	valley
cowboy	berry
penny	address
butterfly	story
daisy	bunch
foot	branch

1. The _____ began work at dawn.

2. From the mountains, they could see the green _____ below.

3. White and yellow _____ were all over.

4. A dog chased _____ flying by.

5. The _____ got tired from trotting.

6. The men sat on the _____ near the barn.

7. One cowboy rubbed his aching _____.

8. The young _____ wanted to hear about the day.

9. They picked juicy _____ in the morning.

10. They picked _____ of flowers too.

11. One boy climbed on the _____ of a tree.

12. That night, the men told _____ by the campfire.

Bonus: Write the plural form of each word you did not use. Then write the matching plural rules.

Quick Plans: Language Arts • ©The Mailbox® Books • TEC61378 • Key p. 95

Pronouns

Group Work

● Label each card in a class set with a different noun or noun phrase. Stack the cards. Then invite a student to take the top card, read it aloud, and write on the board a sentence using the noun or noun phrase and the corresponding pronoun. Then have the rest of the class signal with a thumbs-up or thumbs-down whether the pronoun and antecedent agree. If the wording is not in agreement, help the child correct the sentence. To repeat the activity, invite a different student to take the top card.

● Label four sheets of paper as shown and post each one in a different corner. Give each student a strip from page 56 and have her read it. Direct the student to determine which reflexive pronoun will correctly complete her sentence and have her stand in the corresponding corner. Then invite each child in turn to read her sentence aloud. Guide students to confirm the accuracy of their classmates' positions.

Centers

● Divide a paper plate into eight sections (spinner) and write a different noun or nouns in each section. A child uses a paper clip and a pencil to spin the spinner. Then he writes two sentences: one using the corresponding noun(s) and the other an appropriate reflexive pronoun. He repeats the process four more times to write five different sets of sentences.

● Program paper strips with sentences that each have an underlined possessive subject. For each sentence, label an index card with a pronoun to replace the underlined text. Then program the backs of the sentence strips with the corresponding pronoun for self-checking. A student reads a sentence and then covers the underlined text with the matching pronoun. Next, she copies the newly formed sentence onto a sheet of paper before flipping over the sentence strip to check her work. She continues with each remaining strip.

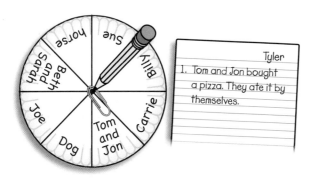

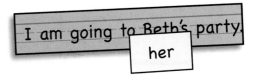

Seatwork See page 57.

Sentence Strips

Use with the second group activity on page 55.

I can do it by _____. TEC61378	She can ride her bike by _____. TEC61378
I am washing _____. TEC61378	Ann went to the fair by _____. TEC61378
I ride the bus by _____. TEC61378	Mary is taking a bath by _____. TEC61378
I like shopping by _____. TEC61378	Kate read the book _____. TEC61378
I talk to _____ when I am nervous. TEC61378	She made the dress _____. TEC61378
I taught _____ to play guitar. TEC61378	She went to swim lessons by _____. TEC61378
I am going to the movies by _____. TEC61378	Jane bought _____ some candy. TEC61378
I saw _____ in the mirror. TEC61378	She walked the dog _____. TEC61378
Can you go to the store by _____? TEC61378	Jim washed the car _____. TEC61378
You should buy _____ a treat. TEC61378	Pete hasn't been _____ lately. TEC61378
Are you going by _____? TEC61378	Steve enjoyed _____ at the party. TEC61378
Can you see _____ in the water? TEC61378	He thinks of _____ as a lucky guy. TEC61378
Be careful you don't hurt _____. TEC61378	He went fishing by _____. TEC61378
You need to give _____ more time. TEC61378	Rob did his homework _____. TEC61378
Are you talking to _____? TEC61378	Did he hurt _____? TEC61378
Please, can you do it _____? TEC61378	He looked at _____ in the mirror. TEC61378

At the Candy Store

To complete each sentence, write the pronoun for each bold word.
Cross out each word as you use it.

herself	myself
themselves	yourself
myself	ourselves
himself	itself
herself	themselves
yourselves	himself

1. **I** am getting candy for _____ .

2. Do **you all** want some for _____ too?

3. **Sarah** picks out some candy for _____ .

4. **Pete** wants to get some candy for _____ .

5. **The candy** is in a barrel by _____ .

6. **Other customers** will buy candy for _____ .

7. **I** am going to buy a lot of candy for _____ .

8. **Pete** is standing by _____ as he waits to get some candy.

9. Will **you** buy _____ some candy too?

10. **We** will buy _____ a lot of different kinds of candy.

11. **She** is getting _____ some chocolates.

12. **Many customers** are buying _____ some candy.

Bonus: Write two more sentences about the candy store. Use the pronouns *yourselves* and *ourselves*.

Quick Plans: Language Arts • ©The Mailbox® Books • TEC61378 • Key p. 95

Verb Tenses

Group Work

● List on the board several verbs that have irregular past tenses; then invite students to write the past tenses. Next, each child divides a sheet of paper into eight sections. The student writes two sentences in each section of his paper: one using the present tense form of a verb and the other using the past tense form of the same verb. To make a booklet, he cuts apart his paper, stacks the resulting pages between two covers, and staples them along the left side. The child titles his booklet before sharing his sentences with a classmate.

● Label half of a supply of cards with different subjects and half with different verbs. Stack the cards in two piles. Lead students in the chant shown as you hold up one card from each stack. When the chant is finished, have students nod their heads if the subject and verb agree or shake their heads if they do not agree. Repeat with the remaining cards.

> A subject and a verb must agree.
> Where's the subject? Where's the verb? Look very carefully.
> Tell me, do this subject and verb agree?

Centers

● Cut ten die-cut shapes in half. On ten of the halves, write a different subject. On the remaining halves, write a different present or past tense verb. (Ensure there is a verb that agrees with each subject.) Place each set of shape halves in a separate container. A child takes a half from each container and determines whether the subject and verb agree. If they do, she matches the halves. If the subject and verb do not agree, she returns each piece to its container and chooses two new halves. The student continues until she has made ten matches.

● Label three paper bags as shown. Cut apart a copy of the cards from page 59 and place each set of cards in the appropriate bag. A child chooses one card from each bag. Then he uses the subject and the verb (in the correct tense) to write a sentence. He repeats the activity until he has five or more sentences.

Seatwork See page 60.

Use with the second center activity on page 58.

we	look	yesterday
TEC61378	TEC61378	TEC61378
I	ask	now
TEC61378	TEC61378	TEC61378
Jon	talk	tomorrow
TEC61378	TEC61378	TEC61378
you	jump	yesterday
TEC61378	TEC61378	TEC61378
the children	walk	now
TEC61378	TEC61378	TEC61378
Sam and Kate	watch	tomorrow
TEC61378	TEC61378	TEC61378
my friend	clean	yesterday
TEC61378	TEC61378	TEC61378
my dad and I	smell	now
TEC61378	TEC61378	TEC61378
the teachers	play	tomorrow
TEC61378	TEC61378	TEC61378

A New Do

Write the correct tense of the verb to match each sentence.

(1) Earlier, Polly _____ to the groomer.
travel

(2) She took her purse and _____ her keys.
grab

(3) She also _____ a magazine before she left.
snatch

(4) Polly _____ a new hairstyle right now!
want

Special: Poodle Perms

(5) The groomer opens a book and _____ Polly some ideas.
show

(6) Polly _____ to a picture that she likes.
point

(7) The groomer _____ to wash Polly's hair.
plan

(8) She_____ Polly's hair in rollers.
wrap

(9) The groomer _____ a dryer to style
use
her hair.

(10) When she finished, the groomer _____
inform
Polly she looked beautiful.

(11) Polly _____ the groomer
thank
and left.

(12) Right now, Polly _____ like
look
a princess!

Bonus: Look at the verb you wrote in each sentence. Color the rollers by the code.
past tense = red
present tense = yellow

Adjectives & Adverbs

Group Work

● Have each student copy a simple sentence at the top of a sheet of paper. Next, direct each child to illustrate the sentence in the middle of her paper. After students share their illustrations, lead a discussion about the differences in the pictures that were drawn. Discuss ways to improve the sentence by adding descriptive details. Then instruct each child to rewrite the sentence at the bottom of her paper, adding adjectives and adverbs so that it tells more about the picture she drew.

● Sit with students in a circle and display a picture. Announce a simple sentence about the picture, such as "I have a dog." The student to your right adds an adjective to the sentence as he repeats it. The person to his right adds a second adjective to the sentence as she repeats the new sentence. Continue around the circle until a student either omits an adjective from the sentence or forgets (or is unable) to add one of her own.

Centers

● Gather sets of three similar classroom items that differ by a characteristic, such as size. A student divides a sheet of paper into six sections. Then he chooses a group of three items and thinks of an adjective to describe the items. He compares the items by adding the suffixes -er and -est to the adjective to create comparative words. Then he draws pictures of the items and labels each illustration with the appropriate word. He continues with another group of objects as time allows.

● Cut apart a copy of the patterns on page 62. Code the back of each word circle section with the matching part of speech for self-checking. Then shuffle the word circle sections and place them faceup. A student places each word circle section on a matching part of speech circle. Then she flips over each word circle section to check her work.

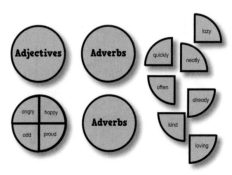

Seatwork See page 63.

Use with the second center activity on page 61.

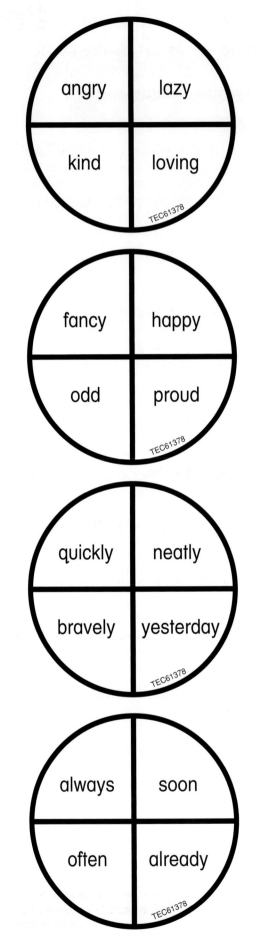

Quick Plans: Language Arts • ©The Mailbox® Books • TEC61378

Catch a Wave

Circle the words by the code.

1. Mike is a great surfer.

2. He has been surfing for nine years.

3. He competes for the gold cup.

4. Last year, he almost won the contest.

5. He went home without the grand prize.

6. He nervously waits for the horn.

7. He hears the loud blast.

8. Mike swiftly paddles out to the deep water.

9. He anxiously waits for the next wave.

10. He spies a white crest.

11. Mike carefully turns his board.

12. He gracefully stands.

13. Mike joyfully rides the enormous wave.

14. A bright smile spreads across his soaked face.

15. The crowd cheers wildly when Mike wins.

You will circle 20 words!

Color Code
adjective = red
adverb = blue

Bonus: Draw an arrow from each adjective or adverb to the word it describes.

Capitalization

Group Work

● Have each small group cut apart a copy of the cards on page 65. Write a sentence, such as one of the ones shown, on the board. Provide time for students to discuss the error or errors that need to be corrected and direct one student from each group to hold up the card with the matching rule. Then have a volunteer correct the sentence on the board.

Possible sentences:
I would love to visit los angeles, california.
My favorite holiday is valentine's day.
On thanksgiving day, my family plays football together.
Have you read the book a bad case of stripes?
I like to wash my hair with sudsy locks shampoo.
My favorite book is charlotte's web by E. B. White.
We buy christopher's crispy crust pizza at the grocery store.

● Give each student a sentence strip and randomly assign each child a different letter. Also give each student a card from page 65. Instruct each child to write a sentence with a capitalized word that follows the rule on her card and begins with her assigned letter. (If she is unable to think of a word that demonstrates her assigned rule, have her choose a different rule.) Form small groups and have each child show her sentence while reading it aloud. Then have her choose a group member to name the capitalization rule that the sentence demonstrates.

Centers

● A child divides and labels a ... as shown. Then he searches ... appropriate reading materi... phrases that are examples o... rule. When he finds a word, ... corresponding section of his ... until he finds a predetermine...

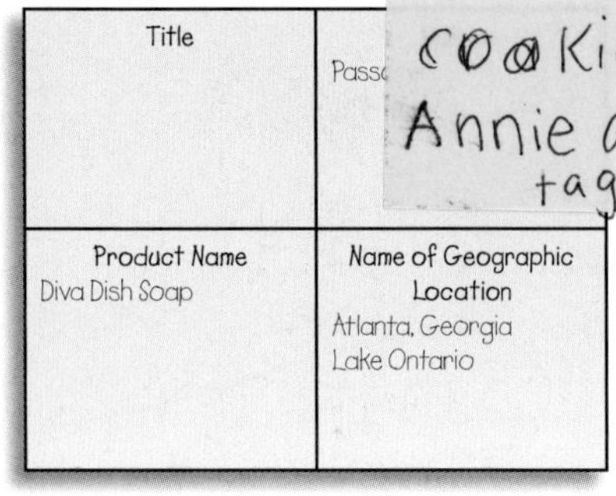

... ds each with a different ... taining a word or words ... that should be capitalized. Use correct ... capitalization in some of the sentences but ... not in others. Put a check mark on the back ... each correct card. A child sorts the cards ... two sets: correctly capitalized and ... apitalized. To check his work, ... each card.

Title	
	Pass...
Product Name Diva Dish Soap	Name of Geographic Location Atlanta, Georgia Lake Ontario

[handwritten note:]
I live in grandview, missouri.
~~knight~~ We ~~eat chocolate~~ ~~tell our family~~ give thanks on Thanksgiving day.
We buy oreos and ~~other~~ cookies at the store.
Annie and jose like to play tag.

[handwritten cards:]
We ... ate Halloween. ✔

We are going to new york for a vacation in may.

Seatwork See page 66.

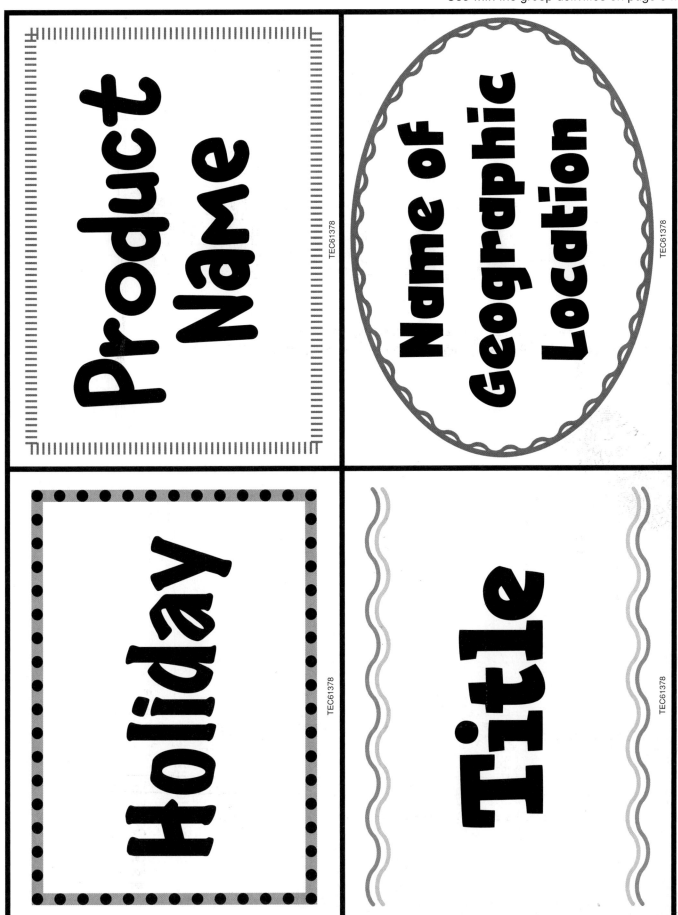

Product Name

TEC61378

Name of Geographic Location

TEC61378

Holiday

TEC61378

Title

TEC61378

66 Name _____

Library Book Picks

Complete each sentence by matching the book title to its reader.
Rewrite the title with capital letters.
Hint: The reader's name and book title will begin with the same letter!

Remember! Book titles should be underlined!

Book titles on shelf:
- creatures of the deep
- jokes are funny!
- let's go, lucy!
- all about dogs
- wait up, waldo
- diary of a boy
- brain freeze
- fairy tales and fables
- the big dinosaurs
- my friend fred
- slimy science
- nine days to better soccer

1. Sam reads *Slimy Science*

2. Ben checks out _____

3. Lindsay is interested in _____

4. Fran finds a book called _____

5. Mary wants to read _____

6. Carla looks up _____

7. On the shelf, Trina sees _____

8. Walter can't wait to read _____

9. Nate's favorite book is _____

10. Ashley chooses _____

11. Derek wants to read _____

12. Justin loves _____

Bonus: Write the titles of three of your favorite books.

Commas

Group Work

● Post a labeled US map and display the rhyme shown. Then form two teams. To play, a student from each team chooses a city from the map and recites the rhyme. Then he writes the name of the city and the state, adding a comma where it is needed. The student consults his team to confirm his work. When both players are finished, check their work and award a point for each correct answer.

> To write an address,
> It's really great
> To remember the order
> City comma state!

● Draw large commas on each of several tagboard triangles. Give each small group a set of commas. Have the students write on the board a portion of a letter or address that uses the number of commas in their set but instruct them not to write the commas. Have each group read its sample aloud and invite classmates to tape the commas where needed.

Centers

● Copy page 68, check the rules you want students to practice, and place the copy in a plastic page protector. Provide a highlighter and a variety of stuffed toy animals and action figures. A child chooses an animal or action figure and refers to the rules to write a letter to it, being sure to include at least one example of each checked rule in the letter. Then he highlights each comma.

● Set out cards labeled with addresses, omitting the comma(s), and transparency pieces labeled with commas. A child chooses a card, adds the comma(s), and then copies the correctly punctuated address onto a sheet of paper.

114 Main Street
Mayberry, NY 09910

Seatwork See page 69.

Comma Rules

☐ Use a comma to write a date.

January 1, 2014   Mar. 17, 2014

☐ Use a comma to separate words in a series.

I like to swim, dance, and run.

☐ Use a comma in a greeting of a letter.

Dear Gramps,

☐ Use a comma in a closing of a letter.

Love,

☐ Use a comma in an address.

Chicago, Illinois

Salt Lake City, UT

I live at 203 South Street, Downingtown, Pennsylvania.

☐ Use a comma to separate what a character says from the rest of the sentence.

"I can't wait for recess," Champ replied.

Dad said, "You need to clean your room."

"If you lend me your crayons," Gil said to me, "I'll share my cookies."

Quick Plans: Language Arts • ©The Mailbox® Books • TEC61378

68   **Note to the teacher:** Use with the first center activity on page 67.

Fan Mail

Add commas where needed.

614 Oak Street
Treetop OH 09954
October 5 2013

Dear Starla
    I just love your music! You are the best singer.

Your friend
Wendy

October 12 2013

Dear Starla,
    When did you learn to play the guitar? You are awesome!

Sincerely
Trey

October 17 2013

Dear Starla
    Remember to get plenty of rest! You have a big show coming up!

Love
Mom

October 19, 2013

Dear Starla
    I went to your concert on June 5 2013. You were amazing!

Your pal
Paige

8550 Main Street
Rocktown CA 09941
October 20, 2013

Dear Starla,
    My sister is your biggest fan! Can you send her a picture?

Best regards
Ben

You should add **14** commas!

Bonus: Pretend you are Starla. Write a response to one of the letters.

Inflectional Endings

Group Work

● Write each base word from the list shown on a separate card. Also label two cards with -*ed* and -*ing* and program separate cards with *gg, nn, pp*, and *tt*. Tape the base word cards to the board and place the other cards nearby. To begin, announce a base word and an inflectional ending. A student removes the matching base word from the board while another child takes the ending card. The students hold the cards side by side to make the word, covering the silent *e* with the ending card if needed or inviting another classmate to place a double consonant card between theirs. Then the remaining students spell the final word aloud and name the spelling rule, if any, for joining the base word and the inflectional ending.

wash
call
talk
plant
look
type
name
flap
hug
pin
tip
bat

● Write a different inflectional ending (-*s*, -*ed*, -*ing*) at the top of separate papers and then place each paper in a different area (station). Form three groups and assign each group to a different station. Announce a word to which an inflectional ending might be added. Then have each group combine the word with the inflectional ending on their paper and write the new word below its heading. After announcing several words, have each group move to a different station.

Centers

● Cut out a copy of the cards and spinner from page 71 and stack the cards facedown. A child takes a card and reads it. Next, he uses a paper clip and pencil to spin the spinner and attempts to make a word by adding the inflectional ending spun to the word on the card. If a real word is made, he writes the word on a sheet of paper, making any necessary spelling changes. If a real word is not made, he returns the card to the bottom of the stack. Then he takes a new card and spins again.

● Label one side of a plastic chip -*s* and the other -*es*. Also label cards with base words. A student divides and labels a sheet of paper as shown. Then she chooses a card and flips the chip. If the word on the card and the letters on the chip correctly spell the word, she writes it on her chart and sets the card aside. If they do not correctly spell the word, she returns the card to the stack. She tosses the chip again and continues until one column has ten words or until all the cards have been used.

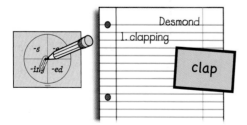

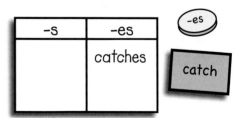

Seatwork See page 72.

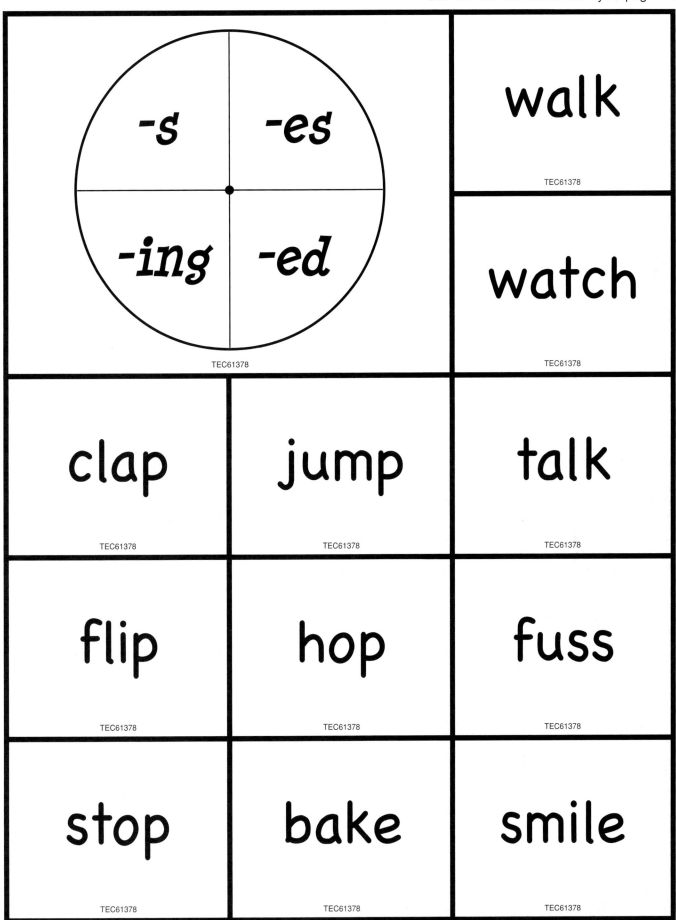

-s   -es
-ing   -ed
TEC61378

walk
TEC61378

watch
TEC61378

clap
TEC61378

jump
TEC61378

talk
TEC61378

flip
TEC61378

hop
TEC61378

fuss
TEC61378

stop
TEC61378

bake
TEC61378

smile
TEC61378

Name _____

So Many Windows

Add *-ed* or *-ing* to each base word.
Write it in the matching column.

base word	-ed	-ing
1. mix		
2. bake		
3. wash		
4. mail		
5. like		
6. tape		
7. drop		
8. hum		
9. lift		
10. watch		
11. miss		
12. skip		
13. wave		
14. plan		
15. shop		

Hint: Sometimes before adding the ending, you need to drop the final *e* and sometimes you need to double the final consonant.

Bonus: Add *-ed* and *-ing* to the word *cry*. Write to explain what you did before adding the endings.

Quick Plans: Language Arts • ©The Mailbox® Books • TEC61378 • Key p. 96

Apostrophes

Group Work

● On separate craft sticks, write a sentence containing either an underlined possessive noun or an underlined contraction, leaving off the apostrophe. Put the sticks in a container and make a chart like the one shown. Invite a volunteer to choose a craft stick and read the sentence aloud. Direct the group to help the student determine whether the sentence contains a possessive noun or a contraction. Then have the child copy the sentence in the correct column, inserting the apostrophe.

Possessive Noun	Contraction
That is Mike's shirt.	He isn't going to school today.

● Write each child's name on a separate index card and, if desired, glue his picture on the card. Next, copy the object cards from page 74 to make a class supply. Give each student a name card and an object card. Instruct the child to draw on a sheet of paper a picture of the named student interacting with the object. Also have her write a sentence that includes a possessive noun to describe her picture, tracing the apostrophe with a crayon so it stands out. Then invite each child to share her drawing as she reads her sentence aloud.

Centers

● A child divides an index card in half. He draws a person or animal on one half and a suitable possession on the other half. Then he labels each picture with a matching noun. He flips the card over and writes the corresponding possessive noun phrase, being sure to punctuate it correctly. He repeats this process with a second card but this time shows a plural possession.

● Draw an apostrophe on a clothespin. Also label ten or more index cards, each with a different contraction that is missing the apostrophe. A student takes a card and clips the clothespin onto it to show where the apostrophe should be placed. Then she writes the contraction on a sheet of paper. She repeats the steps for each remaining card.

Seatwork See page 75.

Object Cards

Use with the second group activity on page 73.

backpack	apple	pencil
flower	bike	notebook
lunchbox	scooter	watch
shoe	banana	turtle

Name _____

Ready, Set, Swim!

Circle each noun that tells who or what owns something.
Rewrite the phrase using an apostrophe.

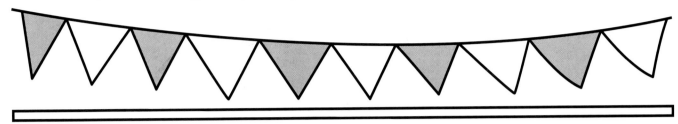

1. color of the (flags) _flags' color_ _____

2. blast of the horn _____

3. caps of the boys _____

4. swimsuit of the girl _____

5. lanes of the swimmers _____

6. whistle of the coach _____

7. time of the stopwatch _____

8. speed of the racer _____

9. bounce of the board _____

10. scores of the divers _____

11. cheers of the fans _____

12. towels of the girls _____

Hint
Is the circled noun singular?

Yes — add 's

No — Does it end in _s_?

Yes — Add '

No — Add 's

Bonus: Draw a star by the singular phrases.

Punctuating Dialogue

Group Work

● Gather interesting pictures and display one. Guide a student to make a statement about the picture as you record his response on the board. Use a different color to write the student's name, the word *said*, and the appropriate punctuation. Invite additional volunteers to share statements about the picture as you record their responses in the same manner. Then display another picture and have each student record a classmate's quote, following the guidelines you modeled.

● Give each group of students a different card from page 77. Have the group work together to rewrite the quote three times. The first time, have students write the speaker's name at the beginning of the quote; the second time, at the end of the quote; and the last time, in the middle of the quotation. Remind students to include the appropriate punctuation. When each group is finished, direct the group members to use a highlighter to trace the punctuation in each quotation.

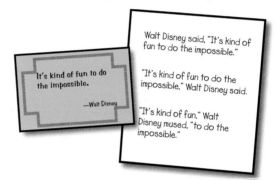

It's kind of fun to do the impossible.

—Walt Disney

Walt Disney said, "It's kind of fun to do the impossible."

"It's kind of fun to do the impossible." Walt Disney said.

"It's kind of fun," Walt Disney mused, "to do the impossible."

Centers

● Place a selection of joke and riddle books at a center, along with a supply of blank paper. A child chooses a joke from a book, rewrites the joke using a different speaker for each part, and inserts the appropriate punctuation.

"What's another name for a clever duck?" Mike asked.

"A wise quacker!" Paul announced.

● Cover the text on one or more pages of a picture book. A child looks at the illustration and writes a dialogue between two or more of the book characters, using appropriate punctuation.

"Where are you going in such a hurry?" the parrot asked.
"I am going to visit my friend Lion," the bear said.
"Why are you going to visit Lion?" the parrot asked.
"Lion is sick," the bear replied.
"Oh! Tell him I hope he feels better," the parrot said.

Seatwork See page 78.

Use with the second group activity on page 76.

Be who you are and say what you feel because those who mind don't matter and those who matter don't mind.

—Dr. Seuss

TEC61378

Be the change you want to see in the world.

—Mahatma Gandhi

TEC61378

If you don't know where you are going, any road will get you there.

—Lewis Carroll

TEC61378

It's kind of fun to do the impossible.

—Walt Disney

TEC61378

Whatever you are, be a good one.

—Abraham Lincoln

TEC61378

Alone we can do so little; together we can do so much.

—Helen Keller

TEC61378

All our dreams can come true, if we have the courage to pursue them.

—Walt Disney

TEC61378

Once you learn to read, you will be forever free.

—Frederick Douglass

TEC61378

Just a Joke

Rewrite the conversation between the bowling ball and pin.
Use correct punctuation.

"How's your game today?" the pin asked.

_____

_____

_____

_____

_____

_____

_____

Bonus: Write a conversation you had with someone recently. Use correct punctuation.

Quick Plans: Language Arts • ©The Mailbox® Books • TEC61378 • Key p. 96

Producing Sentences

Group Work

- List five topics on the board. Have students write two sentences about each topic, directing them to write each sentence on a separate paper strip. Group students and have each group stack its strips facedown. To begin, one child in each group turns over the first five strips; then the group members silently read the sentences on the strips. If a child thinks he can combine two of the sentences, he says, "Connect!" and picks up the two strips. Then he reads the new sentence aloud. If the group members agree that his sentence is a good one, he keeps the two strips; if not, he returns them to the stack. Each group continues until no further matches can be made.

- Display cards labeled with some of the conjunctions shown. Then write two simple sentences on the board. Direct each student to use one of the conjunctions to join the two sentences. Have each child write the new compound sentence on a sheet of paper. Invite volunteers to share the different sentences they made.

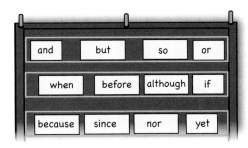

Centers

- ***Partner Game:*** Set out a copy of page 80 and its answer key (page 96), two-sided game markers, a pencil, and a paper clip. Player 1 spins the spinner. He finds on the grid a matching phrase or sentence, puts a marker on the space, and has his partner check the key. If his choice is incorrect, he removes the marker. Then Player 2 takes a turn. The first player to mark five squares in a vertical or horizontal row wins.

- Write simple sentences and conjunctions on separate index cards. Punch holes on the left and right sides of each card. Provide plastic links. A child uses the links to connect two simple sentences and a conjunction. Then she writes the compound sentence on a sheet of paper, correcting the capitalization and punctuation.

Seatwork See page 81.

Cover Up!

A great day. (1)	I am going to school today. (2)	Are you going to the store? (3)	Where is? (4)	Got my book. (5)
We are at the library. (6)	Some apples. (7)	Will you get me some chips? (8)	Who is going with you? (9)	Play outside. (10)
What will we do today? (11)	Can I have? (12)	My friend. (13)	Can we play outside? (14)	I will go on the. (15)
The slide. (16)	He can push you on the swings. (17)	At the park. (18)	She will go to the park with you. (19)	My favorite place. (20)
I am having so much fun! (21)	Swinging high! (22)	How long? (23)	It is almost time to go home. (24)	Let's go home! (25)

Spinner:
- complete sentence
- sentence fragment
- complete sentence
- sentence fragment

Quick Plans: Language Arts • ©The Mailbox® Books • TEC61378 • Key p. 96

Note to the teacher: Use with the first center activity on page 79.

Block That Goal

Join the two sentences to make a compound sentence. Use *and*, *but*, or *so*. Write the new sentence.

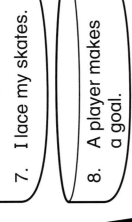

7.	I lace my skates.
8.	A player makes a goal.
9.	The shot is blocked.
10.	I play it all the time.
11.	The horn blasts loudly.
12.	The other team gets it.

1, 10. I love hockey, so I play it all the time.

2, 7. _____

3, 6. _____

4, 9. _____

5, 12. _____

8, 11. _____

1.	I love hockey.
2.	I put on my sweater.
3.	A player steps on the ice.
4.	A player shoots the puck.
5.	A player passes the puck.
6.	He skates to the net.

Bonus: Write two simple sentences about a different sport. Join them to make a compound sentence. Write the new sentence.

Multiple-Meaning Words

Group Work

- Write on the board multiple-meaning words that are easy to illustrate. Guide students to discuss the different definitions for each word. Then each child chooses a word from the list and writes it on a 2" x 3" paper strip. Next, he folds a sheet of paper in half, unfolds it, and illustrates on the top half one of the word's meanings. He turns the paper upside-down and illustrates another meaning on that half. Finally, the child attaches the word strip to the middle of his paper with a brad.

Multiple-Meaning Words

back	bank	bark	bill	bug
count	date	duck	fair	fan
hide	jam	kid	left	nail
open	park	point	pop	press
right	ring	seal	spot	stick
trunk	whistle			

- Display a list of words that have multiple meanings. Next, have each child cut apart the booklet cover and pages from a copy of page 83. The student writes a different word on each page and then writes and draws two different meanings of each word. She stacks her pages beneath the booklet cover and staples them together.

Centers

- Write a different multiple-meaning word on each of ten cards. Then, on each of ten additional cards, write a sentence reflecting one meaning of each word, inserting a blank in place of the featured word. A child matches each word card to the corresponding sentence card. Then he writes a sentence using a different meaning of each featured word.

- Provide a class supply of cupcake liners and paper plates. A student writes a multiple-meaning word on a cupcake liner and then looks up the word in a dictionary. Next, she divides a plate into two or more sections and glues the cupcake liner in the center of the plate. Then the child writes a different definition for the word in each section.

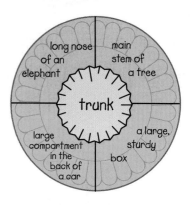

Seatwork See page 84.

Piecing Together Multiple-Meaning Words

by _____

Quick Plans: Language Arts • ©The Mailbox® Books • TEC61378

Word:

What it can mean: What it can mean:

Word:

What it can mean: What it can mean:

Word:

What it can mean: What it can mean:

Word:

What it can mean: What it can mean:

Word:

What it can mean: What it can mean:

Under Construction

Circle the letter to show the meaning of the underlined word.

1. Please pass me the <u>plan</u> for the tree house.
   C. diagram   D. purpose

2. Let me <u>check</u> the supply list.
   T. look at   S. bill showing an amount due

3. I know the perfect <u>place</u> to build it.
   O. put somewhere   A. location

4. Just <u>stick</u> those tools over there.
   L. woody part of a tree   N. set or place

5. Don't you just love the <u>smell</u> of freshly cut wood?
   U. breathe in   O. scent

6. I will need a lot of <u>screws</u>.
   T. twists   S. nails with a spiral groove

7. First, I will <u>drill</u> some holes.
   U. make a hole   I. practice

8. We will hang a <u>tire</u> swing from that tree limb.
   M. wear out   R. rubber wheel

9. You should be able to <u>swing</u> later.
   B. move back and forth   F. type of jazz music

What do you call a snake that builds?

To solve the riddle, write each circled letter from above on
its matching numbered line or lines below.

"
___ ___ ___ ___ ___ ___ ___ ___ ___ ___ ___ ___ ___ ___ ___ "
 3   9   5   3   1   5   4   6   2   8   7   1   2   5   8

Bonus: Choose three underlined words. Write a sentence for each using its other meaning.

Root Words and Affixes

Group Work

● Write a different word from the list shown on each of 30 adhesive labels. Have each child attach a label to his shirt. (If you have fewer than 30 students, give some children more than one label.) Also give each child a copy of page 86. Then direct students to walk around and look at their classmates' labels. Have each child write a word from a classmates' label in the appropriate box on his grid, writing his classmates' initials in the box below and then continuing until he has completed his grid.

Word List

pre-	re-	dis-	un-	mis-
preview	reread	disagree	unskilled	misspelled
preheat	redo	disappear	unable	mislead
preseason	rearrange	dishonest	unusual	misplace
prepaid	reheat	disobey	uneasy	misuse
preschool	refill	disrespect	uncut	misbehave
presoak	replay	distrust	uneven	misunderstand

● Display a list of common base words and briefly discuss the meanings of the words. Have each group write a word from the list on a colorful paper circle (flower center). Then instruct each group to brainstorm different words that use the chosen base word and write each word on a separate petal cutout. After gluing the petals around the flower center, each group posts its flower on a display titled "From Roots to Flowers: Words Have Power!"

Centers

● List on chart paper adjectives that end with a consonant and *y*. Also provide index cards, colorful paper strips, and markers. A child takes three cards and copies a different word onto each card. Next, he writes an *i* on each paper strip, glues a strip to each card, and writes either *-est* or *-er* after the *i*. Then the child turns each card over and uses the comparative or superlative adjective from the other side in a sentence.

● Provide two small paper plate spinners labeled like the ones shown. A child uses a pencil and paper clip to spin each spinner. Then she makes a word using the base word and the affix she spun. If a real word is made, she writes the word and its definition on a sheet of paper. She continues as time allows.

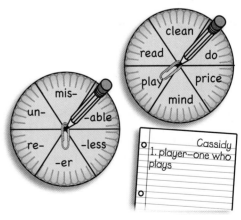

Seatwork See page 87.

pre-	re-	dis-	un-	mis-
view before	read again	to fail to agree	not skilled	to spell incorrectly
heat before	do again	to pass from view	not able	to lead the wrong way
before the season	arrange again	lack of truth or honesty	not usual	to put in a wrong place
paid before	heat again	to fail to obey	not easy	to use incorrectly
before school	fill again	lack of respect	not cut	to behave wrongly
soak before	play again	lack of trust	not even	to fail to understand

Quick Plans: Language Arts • ©The Mailbox® Books • TEC61378

Note to the teacher: Use with the first group activity on page 85.

Keeping Dry

Add the prefix *dis, re,* or *un* to each base word.

1. _____usual

2. _____write

3. _____sure

4. _____obeyed

5. _____visit

6. _____equal

7. _____likely

8. _____read

9. _____pleased

10. _____trace

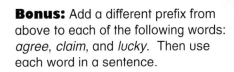

dis = the opposite of
re = to do again
un = not

Bonus: Add a different prefix from above to each of the following words: *agree, claim,* and *lucky.* Then use each word in a sentence.

Complete each sentence with a word from above.

11. The mice _____ the rules when they went far into the woods.

12. They saw many strange and _____ sights.

13. When it started to rain, Mia said, "It's _____ that we will stay dry."

14. Max was _____ what they should do next.

15. "Let's wait under here until we can _____ our steps and go back home!" Max said.

Figurative Language

Group Work

● Title a large bucket as shown. Review with students different types of figurative language, such as metaphors, similes, and idioms. Give each small group a supply of sticky notes and have them scan a current reading selection to find and list on each note a different example of figurative language. Invite each group to share its findings with the class; then display the sticky notes on the bucket.

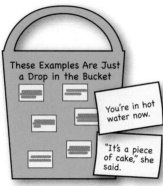

These Examples Are Just a Drop in the Bucket

You're in hot water now.

"It's a piece of cake," she said.

● Program index cards with different figurative language phrases. For each phrase, write the nonliteral meaning on another card. Tape the cards facedown on the board to make a Concentration game grid. Then form two teams. A player from Team 1 takes two cards and reads them aloud. If they make a match, he keeps the cards for his team. If they do not match, he returns them to the board. Alternate play continues as time allows or until all cards are removed. The team with more cards wins.

Centers

● Set out a copy of page 89. A child divides a sheet of paper into four sections. Then she writes a different sentence starter from the list in each section of her paper. She completes each sentence with a simile or a metaphor and then adds an illustration.

The man is as strong as an ox.

The flowers in the meadow are a rainbow.

The baby chick is a fluff of cotton.

The water is as smooth as silk.

● Provide a list of idioms. A student folds an index card in half and then writes an idiom from the list on the front flap of the card. He writes the meaning on the inside flap. The child writes on a sheet of paper a sentence that uses the idiom, gluing the folded card in place of the idiom as shown. Finally, he illustrates his work.

My new bike cost an arm and a leg. a lot of money.

Seatwork See page 90.

Sentence Starters

- The car is as noisy as...
- The kitten's fur is as soft as...
- The girl's laughter is...
- The flowers in the meadow are...
- The water is smooth like...
- The rising moon is...
- The chips are salty like...
- The sand is sparkly like...
- The tiny mouse...
- The baby is as sweet as...
- The man is as strong as...
- The shining sun...
- The horse is...
- The tree is as tall as...
- The girl's blowing hair is...
- The baby chick...
- The book is...
- The ocean is...

Quick Plans: Language Arts • ©The Mailbox® Books • TEC61378

Note to the teacher: Use with the first center activity on page 88.

Midway Fun

Complete each sentence with a simile.
Use the word bank.

Word Bank
lion
rainbow
tree
silk
ice
thunder
spinning top
diamonds
arrow
sea
fluffy cloud
nightmare

1. Today I feel as brave as a _____.

2. The sky is as blue as the _____.

3. That ride was scary like a _____.

4. Now I'm as dizzy as a _____.

5. The roller coaster is tall like a _____.

6. The midway is as loud as _____.

7. The balloons are as colorful as a _____.

8. I threw the dart as straight as an _____.

9. That soda is as cold as _____.

10. The cotton candy is like a _____.

11. The water sparkles like _____.

12. The stuffed animal is as soft as _____.

Bonus: Rewrite the following sentence using a simile:
We are happy at the amusement park.

Quick Plans: Language Arts • ©The Mailbox® Books • TEC61378 • Key p. 96

Word Choice

Group Work

● Say a sentence using commonly overused words, such as "The big dog ran fast," and gently toss a small foam ball to a child. The student holding the ball repeats the sentence, changes one word to a more specific word choice, and says the revised sentence out loud. Then he gently tosses the ball to a classmate. The next child follows the same process. When no more words can be changed in the sentence, introduce a new sentence.

● Form groups and give each group an adjective card from page 92, a thesaurus, a permanent marker, and a different-colored pencil. Each group generates a list of adjectives that are more specific than the one on the card. Next, each group uses the marker to write and order three of these words on the card so the list gets more specific with each successive word. Then each group lightly shades the first section of its card with the colored pencil and gradually colors each subsequent section darker moving down the card.

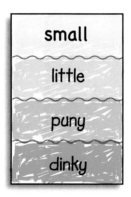

Centers

● Provide yellow construction paper circles, yellow construction paper strips, and a list of common verbs. A student writes a verb from the list on a circle. Then she writes a different synonym for the verb on three or more paper strips. Finally, she glues each paper strip around the circle so they look like rays of the sun.

● Divide 18 plastic cups into three equal sets. On each set of cups, write words with similar meanings. Scramble the cups. A child sorts and stacks the cups with similar meanings as shown. When she is finished stacking, she lists each set of words on a sheet of paper.

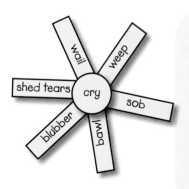

Common Verbs

carry	hold
laugh	make
run	turn
cry	dive
eat	find
help	hit
like	move
say	walk
cut	drink
fall	give

Seatwork See page 93.

Adjective Cards

Use with the second group activity on page 91.

pretty	nice
	TEC61378
good	big
	TEC61378
clean	sad
	TEC61378
happy	small
	TEC61378

(TEC61378 appears on each card)

Out of the Park

Complete the chart.
Use specific words or phrases.

Word	More Specific Word	Most Specific Word or Phrase
shouted	screamed	bellowed
went		
saw		
drink		
snack		
game		
pretty		
happy		
good		
fast		
store		
room		

Bonus: Choose three words or phrases from the last column of the chart. Use each word or phrase in a sentence.

Answer Keys

Page 6

1. A	13. F
2. S	14. J
3. F	15. G
4. C	16. D
5. V	17. O
6. P	18. W
7. H	19. U
8. B	20. A
9. U	21. D
10. A	22. B
11. R	23. M
12. Y	24. R

"ROCK-ET" UNTIL IT GOES TO SLEEP.

Bonus: They are both long *a* words. They have different spelling patterns. Long *a* is spelled *a_e* in *shade* and *ai* in *wait*.

Page 9

1. today	13. player
2. crayon	14. waist
3. snail	15. daisy
4. sprain	16. eighty
5. eighteen	17. subway
6. spray	18. trail
7. clay	19. delay
8. grain	20. eighth
9. outweigh	21. maybe
10. raisin	22. daylight
11. hail	23. neighbor
12. eight	24. weightless

1. eighty	4. trail
2. spray	5. daisy
3. delay	6. neighbor

Bonus: *ai* words—*snail, sprain, grain, raisin, hail, waist, daisy, trail*; *ay* words—*today, crayon, spray, clay, player, subway, delay, maybe, daylight*; *eigh* words—*eighteen, outweigh, eight, eighty, eighth, neighbor, weightless*

Page 12

1. number	2. absent	3. summer
4. pencil	5. cabin	6. sister
7. happy	8. insect	9. finish
10. napkin	11. contest	12. basket

1. true	3. false
2. true	4. false

Bonus: spin|ach, sub|tract, wag|on, vel|vet, fun|ny

Page 15

Flo makes the __very__ best pies. She puts so many fresh __berries__ in them! Some __people__ say that (one) piece of pie isn't __enough__. They __love__ Flo's pies and __always__ ask for more. Today, someone ordered __only__ (one) piece of berry __pie__. When that piece was (gone), she asked for another. She ended up eating the __whole__ pie. In the end, she was __full__ and the pie plate __was__ empty.

Answers will vary but should include that *one* and *gone* do not follow a familiar spelling pattern because they do not have long-vowel sounds as other silent *e* words do.

Bonus: Answers will vary.

Page 18

◖ dislike
⊖ helpful
⊙ mismatched
◗ neatness
⬭ painless
⬭ preheat
⊖ quickly
● restart
☺ sweetest
⊗ unafraid

	1. unafraid
	2. quickly
	3. restart
	4. preheat
	5. helpful
	6. sweetest
	7. dislike
	8. mismatched

Bonus: Sentences will vary but should use the words *painless* and *neatness*.

Page 21

Order may vary. Possible answers include the following:
-*able*: *breakable*, capable of being broken; *governable*, capable of being governed; *manageable*, capable of being managed; *playable*, capable of being played; *printable*, capable of being printed; *workable*, capable of being worked
-*er*: *breaker*, one that breaks; *cheerleader*, one who leads cheers; *player*, one who plays; *printer,* one who prints; *sprinter*, one who sprints; *traveler*, one who travels; *worker*, one who works
-*ment*: *government*, act of governing; *improvement*, act of improving; *management*, act of managing; *measurement*, act of measuring; *movement*, act of moving

Bonus: Answers will vary.

Page 33

1. 34
2. 9, 50
3. 6, 10, 33
4. Any two of the following: blue jays, 34; ducks, 36; finches, 35; penguins, 50; robins, 34; seagulls, 38; storks, 40; swans, 59
5. 36, 42
6. 25, 26, 27, 55
7. 16, 18, 22
8. 5, 6

Bonus: Answers will vary.

Page 36

The main idea wording will vary.

Main idea: Whales are great swimmers.	Main idea: Whales have an excellent sense of hearing.
Whales have smooth skin that slides through water.	Some whales attract other whales by making sounds.
Many whales can swim very fast.	Whales can hear high and low sounds.
Whales can hold their breath underwater for a long time.	Some whales use sounds to find objects underwater.
Strong muscles in a whale's tail help it swim quickly.	People cannot hear some sounds that whales can hear.

Bonus: Answers will vary.

Page 51

	People	Things
1. family	People	Things
2. company	family	grove
3. grove	company	set
4. set, bunch	committee	bunch
5. committee	staff	deck
6. deck	class	fleet
7. fleet	club	collection
8. collection	team	bundle
9. bundle		
10. staff		
11. class, club		
12. team		

Bonus: Sentences will vary.

Page 54

1. cowboys
2. valleys
3. daisies
4. butterflies
5. horses
6. benches
7. feet
8. children
9. berries
10. bunches
11. branches
12. stories

Bonus: pennies; If a word ends with a consonant and *y*,
change the *y* to *i* and add *es*.
addresses; If a word ends with *s*, add *es*.

Page 57

1. myself
2. yourselves
3. herself
4. himself
5. itself
6. themselves
7. myself
8. himself
9. yourself
10. ourselves
11. herself
12. themselves

Bonus: Answers will vary.

Page 60

1. traveled
2. grabbed
3. snatched
4. wants
5. shows
6. points
7. plans
8. wraps
9. uses
10. informed
11. thanked
12. looks

Bonus:
1. red		7. yellow	
2. red		8. yellow	
3. red		9. yellow	
4. yellow		10. red	
5. yellow		11. red	
6. yellow		12. yellow	

Page 63

1. great (red)
2. nine (red)
3. gold (red)
4. last (red), almost (blue)
5. grand (red)
6. nervously (blue)
7. loud (red)
8. swiftly (blue), deep (red)
9. anxiously (blue), next (red)
10. white (red)
11. carefully (blue)
12. gracefully (blue)
13. joyfully (blue), enormous (red)
14. bright (red), soaked (red)
15. wildly (blue)

Bonus: 1. surfer 2. years 3. cup 4. year, won 5. prize 6. waits 7. blast
8. paddles, water 9. waits, wave 10. crest 11. turns 12. stands
13. rides, waves 14. smile, face 15. cheers

Page 66

1. Slimy Science
2. Brain Freeze
3. Let's Go, Lucy!
4. Fairy Tales and Fables
5. My Friend Fred
6. Creatures of the Deep
7. The Big Dinosaurs
8. Wait Up, Waldo
9. Nine Days to Better Soccer
10. All About Dogs
11. Diary of a Boy
12. Jokes Are Funny!

Bonus: Answers will vary.

Page 69

> 614 Oak Street
> Treetop, OH 09954
> October 5, 2013
>
> Dear Starla,
> I just love your music! You are the best singer.
>
> Your friend,
> Wendy

> October 12, 2013
>
> Dear Starla,
> When did you learn to play the guitar? You are awesome!
>
> Sincerely,
> Trey

> October 17, 2013
>
> Dear Starla,
> Remember to get plenty of rest! You have a big show coming up!
>
> Love,
> Mom

> October 19, 2013
>
> Dear Starla,
> I went to your concert on June 5, 2013. You were amazing!
>
> Your pal,
> Paige

> 8550 Main Street
> Rocktown, CA 09941
> October 20, 2013
>
> Dear Starla,
> My sister is your biggest fan! Can you send her a picture?
>
> Best regards,
> Ben

Bonus: Answers will vary.

Page 72

1. mixed   mixing
2. baked   baking
3. washed   washing
4. mailed   mailing
5. liked   liking
6. taped   taping
7. dropped   dropping
8. hummed   humming
9. lifted   lifting
10. watched   watching
11. missed   missing
12. skipped   skipping
13. waved   waving
14. planned   planning
15. shopped   shopping

Bonus: cried, crying; To add -ed, change the -y to i.
To add -ing, do not change the base word.

Page 75

1. flags' color
2. horn's blast
3. boys' caps
4. girl's swimsuit
5. swimmers' lanes
6. coach's whistle
7. stopwatch's time
8. racer's speed
9. board's bounce
10. divers' scores
11. fans' cheers
12. girls' towels

Bonus: 2, 4, and 6–9 should have stars drawn.

Page 78

"How's your game today?" the pin asked.
"Not too bad!" the ball said.
"I have a new joke," the pin announced.
"Let's hear it!" the ball exclaimed.
"Why did the bowling pins stop working?" the pin asked.
"I don't know," the ball replied.
"They were on strike," the pin said.
"Very funny!" the ball said.

Bonus: Answers will vary.

Page 80

1. fragment
2. complete sentence
3. complete sentence
4. fragment
5. fragment
6. complete sentence
7. fragment
8. complete sentence
9. complete sentence
10. fragment
11. complete sentence
12. fragment
13. fragment
14. complete sentence
15. fragment
16. fragment
17. complete sentence
18. fragment
19. complete sentence
20. fragment
21. complete sentence
22. fragment
23. fragment
24. complete sentence
25. complete sentence

Page 81

Conjunctions will vary.

1, 10. I love hockey, so I play it all the time.
2, 7. I put on my sweater, and I lace my skates.
3, 6. A player steps on the ice, and he skates to the net.
4, 9. A player shoots the puck, but the shot is blocked.
5, 12. A player passes the puck, but the other team gets it.
8, 11. A player makes a goal, so the horn blasts loudly.

Bonus: Sentences will vary.

Page 84

1. C
2. T
3. A
4. N
5. O
6. S
7. U
8. R
9. B

A BOA "CONSTRUCTOR"

Bonus: Answers will vary.

Page 87

1. un
2. re
3. un
4. dis
5. re
6. un
7. un
8. re
9. dis
10. re
11. disobeyed
12. unusual
13. unlikely
14. unsure
15. retrace

Bonus: disagree, reclaim, unlucky; Sentences will vary.

Page 90

1. lion
2. sea
3. nightmare
4. spinning top
5. tree
6. thunder
7. rainbow
8. arrow
9. ice
10. fluffy cloud
11. diamonds
12. silk

Bonus: Answers will vary.